A GUIDE TO GOOD HEALTH

Healthy in Body, Mind & Spirit

MENTAL HEALTH

LETTERS AND TALKS OF THE LUBAVITCHER REBBE,
RABBI MENACHEM M. SCHNEERSON

Compiled and Translated by
Rabbi Sholom Ber Wineberg

SICHOS IN ENGLISH
788 Eastern Parkway | Brooklyn, New York 11213

SICHOS IN ENGLISH

HEALTHY IN BODY, MIND AND SPIRIT
– MENTAL HEALTH –

Second Edition — April 2021

Typography, template, and cover design by Spotlight Design

ISBN 978-1-9381-6314-2

CONTENTS

FOREWORD

Seventeen-year-old Sara Posner[1] was torn. With multiple options for what to do the following year, she had come to the Rebbe seeking guidance and clarity. Should she teach at her father's school in Pittsburgh or accept an offer from a school in New York? Should she travel to Eretz Yisrael or perhaps join her sister Bessie in Milan, where she and her husband served as Chabad emissaries?

She waited nervously for her first private audience, worried about how she would begin explaining everything.

Then her turn came, and the door opened. As she walked in, the Rebbe was sitting behind his desk, writing something, and he lifted his head. "Good evening, Miss Posner," he said. Sara, surprised, just burst out laughing and felt instantly at ease. The Rebbe asked her many questions — including why she looked so unwell — and she explained that she was studying very hard for final exams, and also teaching in another school. The Rebbe gave her a blessing that she should be successful in all her endeavors. He also told her not to worry about what to do next year; just to take some time off and relax.

Sara left the audience relieved, and with a warm feeling of support and reassurance. "I felt like I was walking on a cloud," she relates.

---

1 Now Sasonkin.

At the end of that summer, the Rebbe told her parents that she should go to Milan to help her sister. As only married couples were sent at the time as the Rebbe's emissaries abroad, Sara was honored and excited to be an exception to the rule. At the same time, she was a little concerned about not knowing the language. The Rebbe said, however, that it would be okay because she would be working with small children, and language would not be a barrier.

Sara came to Milan and taught kindergarten. She was working seven days a week [with responsibilities for children's Shabbos gatherings], and also trying to learn Italian. After a few months of this, she began to feel quite overwhelmed by the amount of pressure she was under. This led to her feeling insecure and unsuccessful, as well as underappreciated. And so she wrote a long, very emotional letter to the Rebbe about it.

In reply, she received a long and most amazing letter — sent by special delivery.[2] This letter is illustrative of much of the Rebbe's sensitive and nuanced approach to mental and emotional wellbeing. One can discern many lessons from the Rebbe's response to one seventeen-year-old girl. The following are some examples, as well as their relevant excerpts:

The Rebbe validates challenges to one's mental and emotional state as a natural and very real part of the human condition:

Since one is only human, it is not unusual to relapse occasionally into a mood of discouragement...

I trust that since you wrote your letter, your mood and outlook have considerably improved, and that this letter

---

2   Parts of the letter are also brought on page 84. For a firsthand account of Mrs. Sara (Posner) Sasonskin's experience, see Here's My Story (JEM). Additional details have been added after conversation with Mrs. Sasonkin.

will find you in a completely different frame of mind. Nevertheless, I am sending you this letter, since one is only human and subject to changes of mood...

At the same time, the Rebbe strongly rejects the pessimistic perspective she had of herself and her reality, helping her reframe the narrative to one of empowerment. The Rebbe encourages her to do all she can to avoid slipping further into a spiral of negativity:

Needless to say, I was somewhat taken aback by the tone of your letter. It is a good illustration of how it is possible for a person to read and to learn and to receive instruction from books and teachers, and yet when it comes to actual experience all this instruction goes by the wayside.

I refer to the things which you have surely learned in the books of Mussar [Jewish ethical works] and especially Chassidus, about the tactics of the yetzer hara [evil inclination] to instill spirit of depression, discouragement, and despondency in order to prevent the Jewish person from fulfilling his Divine mission . . This is exactly what has happened in your case, and I am surprised that you do not realize it. The proof is that from the information that I have received, I can see that you have accomplished a great deal more than you imagine.

You surely know of the saying of the Baal Shem Tov that a soul comes down to live on this earth for a period of seventy to eighty years for the sole purpose of doing another Jew a single favor materially or spiritually. In other words, it is worthwhile for a Jewish soul to make that tremendous journey and descend from heaven to earth in order to do something once for one fellow Jew.

In your case the journey was only from the USA to Milan and can in no way be compared with the journey of the soul from heaven to earth. And however pessimistic you might feel, even the yetzer hara would have to agree that you have done not only a single favor, but numerous good deeds, and even only your work with the children of the gan [kindergarten] would have justified it...

As for your mentioning the fact that no one seems to be interested in your work, et cetera, surely you will admit that G-d, whose knowledge and providence extends to everyone individually, knows and is interested in what you are doing .. and I need hardly mention that I, too, am interested in your work.

If it seems to you that you have been left to "carry the ball" yourself, it is surely only because there is confidence in you, and that since you have been sent to Milan you undoubtedly have the ability, qualifications and initiative to do your work without outside promptings, et cetera.

The Rebbe also emphasizes the importance of physical self-care and the critical role it plays in one's mental health and consequently spiritual service:

One should also bear in mind, as the Old Rebbe [Rabbi Schneur Zalman] has stated most emphatically in the laws of learning and of teaching children Torah, that a person who is engaged in teaching children Torah should especially take care of his health, since it directly affects the success of the work.

I trust, therefore, that you are looking after yourself in matters of diet and rest, et cetera, and that you will always be in a state of cheerfulness and gladness.

Finally, offering true empathy and understanding, and acknowledging the significant benefit of sharing one's true feelings with another, he invites the young woman to continue doing so in her correspondence with him:

The above should not be understood to mean that if you do find yourself in such a frame of mind, you should try to conceal it and not write about it. For our Sages have said, "when a person is anxious over something, he should relate it to others," for getting something off one's chest is in itself already a relief.

Encouraged by the Rebbe's empathy and responsiveness to her feelings, Sara took the letter to heart and recognized that indeed, her gloomy perception of herself and those around her was a distortion of the reality. She was, in fact, accomplishing a great deal and her efforts were certainly appreciated. She returned to her work with renewed vigor and motivation.

* * *

A HOLISTIC APPROACH

The Rebbe would often quote the words of the Maggid of Mezritch that "a small hole (ailment) in the body, is a big hole in the soul!" In other words, we cannot divorce our physical health from our spiritual health. How much more so is this true when we are dealing with issues of the mind and heart, where the impact of our spiritual health on our mental health and vice versa are self-evident and of tremendous consequence.

The struggles in this arena vary over a huge spectrum. There are those who struggle periodically with moments of doubt, worry and sadness. Many battle more chronic disorders such as clinical depression and anxiety or are confronted by suicidal thoughts.

Amongst the many and varied issues regarding which individuals throughout the world turned to the Lubavitcher

Rebbe for guidance, matters of mental and emotional health rank prominently. Hence the veritable mountain of responses and statements that offer guidance on this subject — through his voluminous correspondence, through answers relayed via his secretariat, through private audiences, and through public pronouncements at the Chassidic gatherings known as farbrengens.

The Rebbe's approach to health and healing is holistic. The Rebbe would take into consideration the physical, mental, and spiritual dimensions of an ailment or of the ailing individual and would advise accordingly.

The Rebbe stressed the critical role of a G-d-centered, moral education in preventing many societal, psychological or physical challenges. Often noting that Torah is a true guide for life — "the Torah of truth, the Torah of life," the Rebbe pleaded with parents, educators and legislators to raise children with a clear sense of G-d's presence and involvement in their lives and His unlimited love for them. The children needed to be empowered with the understanding that they contained a spark of G-d within themselves and therefore they possessed the ability to overcome any obstacles in their path and fulfill their Divine purpose. In the Rebbe's words[3]:

> *The fundamental role of education, and one of its earliest and most important goals is to mold a healthy, productive individual and to safeguard a person against his own potential negative tendencies and offensive traits...*

And in a letter, after noting that it is difficult to advise in matters of psychology and education, as individual circumstances vary[4]:

---

3   Parts of the essay are brought on page 237.

4   The full letter is brought on page 222.

I would like to make one general point which can be universally applied in educational problems...

I refer to the effort to make the children aware that they possess a soul which is a part of G-d, and that they are always in the presence of G-d (as explained in Chapters 2 and 41 of the Tanya).

When this is done persistently, and on a level which is suitable to the age group and background of the children, the children come to realize that they possess a great and holy quality which is directly linked with G-d, the Creator and Master of the world, and that it would therefore be quite unbecoming and unworthy of them to do anything which is not good.

At the same time they come to realize that they have the potential to overcome temptation or difficulty...

The Rebbe drew a clear line between the physical and psychological and the spiritual aspects of healing. Certain matters could be addressed strictly from a spiritual and educational perspective — especially at the preventive stage — while others also necessitated professional medical intervention, especially in order to cure existing mental conditions. The spiritual aspect was not intended to serve as a substitute for the medical treatment; it worked beside it and complemented it.

The following excerpt is one example[5]:

As for the problem of some children having a habit to take things not belonging to them, this may fall into one of two categories:

a. The attitude mentioned in the Mishnah in Pirkei Avos "Mine is thine and thine is mine." In this case the effort

---

5   Ibid.

should be made to educate the child that just as it is
necessary to be careful not to offend or shame another
person, so it is necessary to be careful not to touch
anything belonging to somebody else.

b. *An unhealthy condition which should be treated*
   medically by specialists who know how to handle such
   an aberration.

In the light of the above, it is self-evident that the medical treatment, when needed, would need to support spiritual healing and not detract from it. Thus, the Rebbe urged that professionals seen for the treatment of mental health conditions value belief in G-d and religious practice.

As the Rebbe writes:

In connection to your writing that the said individual
finds himself under the care of a mental healer... There is
a specific class of therapists who commence their therapy
by deriding G-d, spirituality ... and the like. If that is the
type of therapist he is seeing, then even if the therapist is
distinguished in his field, much examination and clarification
is required in order to ascertain whether the benefit he may
receive from him outweighs the long-time harm that may
result [from this form of therapy] with the passage of time.

* * *

HOW TO READ THE RESPONSES

We remind the reader to keep in mind on their journey through the book that most of the material assembled in this work consists of private responses to individuals. The Rebbe addressed each person in the context of their lives, their values, their emotional state and their struggles. At times, the words are soft and compassionate, while to others the Rebbe uses stronger and more demanding language — and at times a combination of the two.

The Rebbe's answer to one individual may not necessarily apply at all to another, for, as the Rebbe once wrote,[6] "It is *patently obvious*[7] that a directive to an individual does not serve at all as a directive to the public, even when the issues are the same."

To address this challenge we have included varied approaches from the Rebbe as quoted from numerous responses. Also, by noting that numerous answers are written in the same vein, we have an indication of the Rebbe's overall approach to a specific issue or matter.

Moreover, some of the responses to individuals may be given in the context of that time period's state of medical advances and accepted practice, particularly since the Rebbe would at times encourage the use of the latest medical advances, procedures, and medications, some of which were the cutting-edge treatments at the time.

Some of the terminology and medical definitions have changed over time as well, and hence the importance to read the letters in the context of the scientific knowledge and vernacular of the times they were written. While many of the letters included in this book are translations from Hebrew or Yiddish, those written in English are reproduced here virtually unchanged, with only minor grammatical edits. The dates or sources cited may be of benefit in addressing the above notes.

In light of all the above, and in keeping with the Rebbe's deeply-held request for every individual to seek the guidance

---

6   In a handwritten response.

7   Emphasis is the Rebbe's.

of a personal mentor in spiritual matters, the reader is encouraged to explore — together with a mentor well versed in the Rebbe's teachings — how the ideas expressed throughout this book might apply to their own life.

* * *

REVISED EDITION

In the early 2000's, Sichos in English published a three-volume series titled *Healthy in Body, Mind, and Spirit: A Guide to Good Health*, whose content — largely excerpts of letters of the Rebbe — focused on issues of health and well-being.

The third volume in the series focused primarily on mental health, with a large percentage of its content focused on inspiring people and advising them how to rise above the challenges of depression, despondency and grief. This revised edition of that third volume has 100 new pages of content and many new other changes.

During the Covid pandemic, there has been a sharp increase in challenges to mental health. Feelings such as loneliness, anxiety, fear and grief are some of the reactions to the circumstances of our time. This has led to a surge in individuals seeking guidance, help, support and medical intervention for their mental and emotional well-being.

The Rebbe's advice in this area is invaluable. This is why we embarked on publishing a second and revised edition of this volume, where we collected and translated more of the correspondence by the Rebbe addressed to those who reached out to him sharing their questions concerning their struggles, pain and even hopelessness at times.

* * *

IN GRATITUDE

The first edition was compiled and translated by Rabbi Sholom Ber Wineberg, who also translated the additional letters included in this new volume. The editing was done by Rochel Chana Schilder, with editorial assistance by Uri Kaploun. Yosef Yitzchok Turner designed the layout and typography for both editions, and Rabbi Yonah Avtzon, OBM, prepared the text for publication.

For the revised edition, a team of researchers added additional sources from the Rebbe's letters, and the formatting and design of the publication was revamped by Spotlight Design to provide an easier reading experience.

We thank the following individuals for their contributions to this second edition: Rabbi Levi Avtzon, Rabbi Motti Seligson, Zalmy Avtzon, Motti Diskin, Meir Avtzon, Mrs. Chanie Wolf and Chaya Berger; Rabbi Shmuly Avtzon for leading and managing the project from start to finish.

For some of the new content we thank Kehot Publication Society, Chabad.org, A Chassidisher Derher magazine, JEM and the many individuals who published and contributed to journals over the years containing the Rebbe's advice and guidance concerning mental health.

* * *

In a letter to a family who suffered a tragedy the Rebbe writes[8]: "May G-d bless you in all matters that you require, among the most important of them true serenity and peace of mind. May He bless you that your life be such that matters will be good for you in all aspects, including goodness that is overtly revealed and intellectually comprehensible."

---

8 cf page 35.

May we merit to witness this beautiful blessing in our lives; and may we witness the fulfillment of Isaiah's prophecy that "G-d will wipe tears from all faces"[9], with the coming of Mashiach who will usher in the complete redemption — a time of true serenity, peace and clarity — speedily in our days, Amen!

Sichos In English

Pesach Sheni, 14th of Iyar, 5781

---

9   *Yeshayahu 25:8.*

chapter 1

COPING WITH TRAGEDY, MISFORTUNE AND LIFE'S ADVERSITIES

THE ROAD TO
LEADING A SATISFIED LIFE

...Notwithstanding the mode and content of your letter, and moreover, notwithstanding that this situation repeats itself in every letter I receive from you, I have not, G-d forbid, given up hope, that ultimately you will see not only the goodness in life, including *your* life, but also truly feel this in your heart. Particularly — using the language of *Chassidus* — since in our world everything is an admixture of good and evil and it is up to man to choose what he will put his emphasis on, what he will contemplate, and what will be his area of interest.

For in the life of every individual there are two paths, to see the good that envelops him, or.... If this is so concerning all human beings, how much more so does this apply to Jewish sons and daughters who believe with absolute faith in the eternality of the soul, i.e., the eternality of the spiritual, i.e., its ultimate and complete victory [over negative forces]. For it is verily impossible that something fleeting and passing not be completely vanquished by that which is enduring and everlasting, inasmuch as the two are incomparable.

We learn from the tale related by our Sages that Adam, even before he was banished from *Gan Eden*, complained about his situation, and he was deemed an ingrate. Conversely, Jewish sons and daughters who were in German — *yemach shemam* — concentration camps, during the most horrific of times, recited the morning blessings, etc., thanking and blessing the Creator and Conductor of the world. Ultimately, each of us finds himself within these two extremes.

...The point being: The manner and quality of a person's life, whether it will be a life replete with satisfaction and meaningful content, or the opposite thereof, is to a very great extent dependent on the person's own desire, for it controls the mind's eye, whether it will see the "right side" or the "left side."

(Igros Kodesh, Vol. 20, p. 41)

DEPRESSED MENTAL STATE

...I am in receipt of your letter.

Judging by your writing, I trust it is unnecessary to emphasize to you at length that one of the foundations of our faith and way of life is the firm conviction that G-d's providence extends to everyone individually, and that He is the Essence of Goodness and does only good, as the Torah states, "And G-d saw all that He had done and behold it was very good."[1]

And while G-d gave man freedom of choice to choose his way in life and his daily conduct, He has, in His goodness, given us His Torah, which teaches us what the right way of life is and how to accurately pursue it.

Therefore, your writing that you find life "a burden," and the general mood in which your letter is written, are completely out of harmony with the Jewish way of life.

---

1 *Bereishis* 1:1.

I can, of course, understand that such a mood is possible in light of the events and occurrences that you describe in your letter. However, this is possible only if you do not take into account the fact that everything is by Divine providence, and therefore you think that you are alone in the world and quite forsaken, having only yourself to rely upon, and so on.

On the other hand, if you bear in mind that everything that happens occurs through G-d's providence which affects every single individual, and that the only freedom a person has is freedom [in those matters with which] he personally is concerned but he has no control over events relating to others, then you will view matters in a different light.

Though you may still not understand why such seeming untoward events occur, it will no longer surprise you, knowing the limitations of the human mind and how impossible it is for a human mind to grasp and understand the infinite wisdom of G-d, who is called *Ein Sof* (Infinite).

Consequently, seeing that G-d provided you with the gift of life and other blessings, and at the same time provides you the opportunity to fulfill His will, not because He needs the satisfaction and pleasure of having His will fulfilled, but simply because this is how He makes it possible for a Jew to spread G-d's light in the world at large, and especially in his own family and immediate environment, surely it is out of place to refer to these blessings of G-d as "a burden," G-d forbid.

Nor is it right to consider as burdensome the fact that it is difficult to see the good clearly for, as our Sages declare, "The reward matches the effort."[2] The better and more worthy the object, the harder it is to obtain, and while the difficulties may be imaginary or real, the effort to overcome these difficulties

2 *Avos* 5:21.

will be truly rewarding, and the reward will infinitely surpass the effort. It is surely unnecessary to elaborate further on this subject.

I suggest that you have the *mezuzos* of your home checked, as well as your *tefillin*, if they have not been checked within the past twelve months, and every weekday morning before putting on the *tefillin* you should put aside a small coin for *tzedakah*.

No doubt your wife observes the good custom of putting aside a small coin for *tzedakah* before lighting the candles.

(From a letter of the Rebbe)

SADNESS AND DISILLUSIONMENT

I received your letter in which you briefly describe the hardships you have endured during your lifetime — the wanderings, the [traumatic] experiences, the grief. Finally, you describe your recent arrival in ... and your observations about matters that seem to be inexplicable.

...You wonder — as you write — why there seems to be no explanation for the events that transpired with your family and in your home.

When you will consider this matter a bit, you will realize that there is really no cause for wonder, for a person can only see to a limited extent those events that transpire in his life and around him. It is therefore impossible for him to truly comprehend the events that he perceives.

To make this matter perfectly clear, I will provide you with an example:

Imagine a person entering a hospital operating theater and seeing someone lying on the operating table. People brandishing knives surround him and are cutting him, and the person is groaning with pain. Nevertheless, these people continue with their cutting.

The chance observer, wholly unaware of the concept and purpose of a surgical procedure, will leave the room in an uproar — a human being was forcibly taken and is being cut up; he is groaning with pain and cannot free himself from his tormentors and murderers.

However, when the chance observer is given to understand that the operation is critical in order for the patient to live many more decades, for which reason excessive consideration is not being given to the patient's temporary pain and discomfort during the few hours of the operation, [then his position will change entirely].

The guest observer will not only fully agree that they — the "cutters" — are not tormentors and murderers, but he will now understand that the very opposite is true: they are doing the greatest possible favor to the individual who is under the knife.

And this is so, [i.e., they are truly performing an act of goodness and kindness by operating,] notwithstanding the fact that the surgeon cannot offer a 100% guarantee that the outcome of the surgery will be successful, nor how many more years the patient will live following the surgery — even if the surgery is successful.

We understand from the above that a person may experience in his lifetime a matter that pains him for a period of time — true pain and not imaginary.

That person, however, is also aware of — and moreover,

sees — the Divine Hand of individual providence; i.e., that the world's conduct is not without rhyme or reason and it functions according to a definite system. Moreover, this system encompasses not only himself but also his family, and *so many* others as well.

Normal, healthy and sound intellect then dictates that surely these [seemingly untoward] events do not violate the overall system that prevails in the world around him. It is merely that the individual has not heard from [G-d, the benevolent] "Professor and Surgeon," what great benefit will result from the temporary pain.

There are those who question and say that they doubt that the world has a system and purpose, but everyone knows from physics, chemistry, astronomy, and so on (recognized not only by Jews or by believing people but even by non-believers) that even the smallest atom has its exact rules.

Everything must operate in accordance with the rules: even the earth, rocks, plants and animals, and everything that surrounds us has definitive laws and established methods, even though it is far more complex and vast than one person and his family.

...Imagine that you are in a massive building that has thousands of rooms; the furniture in each room is perfectly arranged. However, in one tiny room with strange furnishings, the sense of organization so obvious in the rest of the structure is not immediately apparent.

Since the gigantic building and its thousands of chambers can be seen as part of an orderly system, undoubtedly the individual room and its unique furnishings are also part of the overall plan. Although the untrained observer may not at first understand the unusual pattern, with some thought he will come to realize that it must also be a part of the larger system.

I feel it would be superfluous to spell out the meaning of the parable. I just wish to add one detail: If each one of us, including you yourself, were to ponder all the events of our lives wherever they occurred, and we would look objectively, we would see that there were tens and thousands of instances where we were led in a certain direction....

Nevertheless, the Holy One desires that a person should do things of his own free will. He therefore allows each person the ability to choose his own path. It is therefore no wonder that being only human, there can be a few occasions when a person falls off the path, and instead of the path being straight, it has some zig-zags.

But if we give it thought and don't fool ourselves, we see to it that the number of zig-zags are as few and infrequent as possible. Then we arrive at the goal which the Holy One has set up for every person and, particularly for each individual, that he and his family should be truly happy.

We can come to this by conducting ourselves according to Torah, which is known as the Torah of Life. We need only be wary of the criticism often used by the evil inclination: he points to a person people believe to be *frum* and who conducts himself according to Torah, and then goes about highlighting that individual's seeming deficiencies.

The evil inclination thus wishes to demonstrate to the person it is seeking to influence that, since [the *frum*] person is one who conducts himself according to Torah and nonetheless has these negative points — the proof being that he did this or that misdeed — then the Torah itself must perforce not be commendable, G-d forbid.

This, however, is of course patently false, for the evil inclination is only presenting one aspect of the person and not the individual as a whole.

[This is illuminated by a story.]

If a person is walking in the street and meets someone leaving a medical specialist's office and the person is using crutches, the passerby could think that the specialist is not good. After all, this person visited him and paid him a lot of money, and is obeying all the doctor's instructions, and he still needs crutches!

But if someone would explain to the passerby that before the patient was in the doctor's care, he couldn't move his feet altogether and was completely paralyzed, then [the passerby] would realize that the doctor had not only reduced the paralysis, but has also strengthened the patient, and enabled him to not only use his feet but even to walk.

As time passes, things improve [for the patient] and it's getting easier, even though he still needs crutches. There may come a time, if he follows the doctor's advice, when he will dispose of the crutches and be completely healed.

The same is true for people. From the time they are born, they [all] have different qualities. Some have more good and some more bad. Through education by good teachers, and above all through self-improvement, provided it is done correctly, these bad traits become weaker and less effective over time.

Since a person has to grow his entire life, it is no wonder that we can meet a person in the middle of his personal growth and development work — his self-training — and still find some of his negative qualities. This is not necessarily because he isn't following the instructions of the "specialist" in his training, rather that by every measure he has weakened and reduced his negative [qualities] compared to his earlier state.

I want to end by expressing my intent in this letter. I don't intend this to be mere philosophy, but rather to implant in you the idea that if you will want to apply your objectivity and good intellect, it should bring you to strengthen your trust in *Hashem* and to look with a positive eye at the people around you in general and the inhabitants of ... especially.

See their positive points, which for the most part they worked hard to develop, and view their negative points, if there are any, in the way we discussed previously with regard to the temporary crutches.

Above all you must know that you must do your part to illuminate and brighten your surroundings, not only your own family, but a larger group of people. This can be achieved by being permeated with love of a fellow Jew. This will benefit all and certainly is good and will achieve goodness for you and your family.

I hope you will read this letter with the appropriate attention. It is self-understood that if you have any questions or lack of understanding, I will be happy for you to write about them and I will answer to the extent I am able, even if because of many obligations the answer may be a little delayed.

I feel also that the occasional delays are also an instruction: that you are being given additional time so that of your own free will you should change your view of the people around you, and come to realize that an individual's conduct is subject to constant improvement, and the A-lmighty should grant you success.

(*Igros Kodesh*, Vol. XIII, p. 170)

SUFFERING, ILLNESS AND DEATH

I duly received your letter, in which you write about various things which you do not understand, such as the suffering of your father, etc.

Judging by your letter, it is surely unnecessary to emphasize to you at length the obvious idea, namely that it is certainly not surprising that a human being does not understand the ways of G-d, for a created and finite being surely cannot understand the Infinite.

The opposite would rather be surprising, and it is only due to G-d's infinite kindness that He has revealed to man certain aspects of His Divine Providence.

There is a simple illustration: It would surely not be surprising that a five-year-old child could not understand the conduct of a great scientist, even though the scientist was at one time a five-year-old boy, and the present five-year-old boy may grow up and become even a greater scientist.

In other words, the five-year-old boy is potentially in possession of all the qualities of the mature scientist, yet it would not be surprising that the five-year-old boy cannot understand the great scientist.

But a created human being has nothing in common with the Creator insofar as intelligence and capacities are concerned. It is only that because of G-d's kindness that certain aspects of G-d's Providence have been revealed to man, including also the question of suffering, where we can use a similar analogy.

When a young child is told to sit down and learn the ABC, and do homework, etc., this deprives him of going out into the fresh air, sometimes interferes with having his meal on time, and might also curtail his sleeping hours, etc.

The child, while complying with these instructions, is not doing so because he realizes their wisdom, but because he has no choice in the matter, since he is compelled by his father or mother or teacher to do this. This is not a case where his freedom is curbed so that he would not go about breaking windows, and the like.

Insofar as the child is concerned, it is for him true suffering to be deprived of fresh air, or rest, etc., which by common consent are considered good things. Nevertheless, of what consideration is the child's temporary suffering, even though it extends for days or months, by comparison with the good which he will enjoy thereby for the rest of his life.

A further point to remember is this: When a person who has been ill succumbs to his illness, it is clear to every normal person that the illness could affect only the physical body. Obviously if there is something wrong, say, with the blood of the patient, it cannot affect the patient's spiritual life and his everlasting soul.

In other words, when a patient succumbs to an illness, this only happens because the union between the soul and the body has come to an end, but the soul is an everlasting one, and this is one of the basic foundations of our Jewish faith, as many other faiths.

In the Torah it is frequently explained and emphasized that life on this earth is only a preparation for the future and everlasting life in the world to come.

This is also taught in the well known Mishnah of *Pirkei avos*, which we read and study these *Shabbos*im. The Mishnah states, "This world is like a vestibule to the future world; prepare yourself in the vestibule so that you can enter the banquet hall" (Perek 4, 21).

Now, when during the time when one is in the vestibule there has been a period of suffering, whereby there will be an infinite gain in the "banquet hall," it will surely be worthwhile.

It is impossible to describe the joys of the life of the soul in the world to come, for even in this world while the soul is connected with the body, its life is on an infinitely higher plane; how much more so when the soul is no longer distracted by the body.

Compare the joy and excitement of a child when he receives a tasty candy, with the joy of a very wise and learned scientist who succeeds in resolving an important scientific problem. Here again, as mentioned before, there is some connection between the child and the scientist, and everything is relative.

But insofar as the life on this earth and the life of the soul in the future world is concerned, the differences are not of degree but of kind, and there is no common denominator between the two.

At the same time it should be remembered that the suffering in the "vestibule," which is no more than a corridor to the "banquet hall," is after all a temporary one, and the gain is eternal.

Of course, you may ask why things are so conditioned that one must give up something in order to gain more. This would be the same as a child asking why he must give up his outdoor pleasures, etc. But surely it is not unkindness to the child to "deprive" him so.

I trust that the above will suffice to answer your question.

(From a letter of the Rebbe, dated 7 Iyar, 5727)

COPING WITH EXTREME BEREAVMENT

The following is the Rebbe's response to an individual who lost his wife, and two months after her demise was still inconsolable and writes to the Rebbe, that "every morning upon arising and seeing that she is not here, I cannot keep myself from crying."

The Rebbe noted the word "crying," and commented: "Crying?!" — That causes pain to her soul, **etc.**, as is easily understood.

Exchange your tears for the recitation of a ***Mizmor*** (chapter) of *Tehillim* (in Hebrew, *Mizmor* means "song"), and one *Mishnah* — specifically doing the above in a manner of joy, as is easily understood.

OVERCOMING DESPONDENCY BY HAVING EMOTIONS ACT IN TANDEM WITH BELIEF AND INTELLECT

...Jewish men and women are generally "believers, sons of believers;" that is to say, they all believe and also comprehend that G-d alone conducts the entire world. Jews also believe with perfect faith that G-d is the Essence of Goodness.

You surely heard as well the saying of my father-in-law, the Rebbe, of blessed memory, who related in the name of the Baal Shem Tov, that G-d loves every Jewish man and woman as a father loves an only child. (In fact, He loves them even more than that; this analogy is used because we cannot imagine a greater love than that of a parent to an only child.)

The upshot of all the above is that all that G-d does is for the good; since G-d desires that things be good for Jews not only spiritually but materially as well, surely His goodness extends not only to the realm of the spiritual, but also to the realm of the material.

As mentioned before, Jews not only believe the above, but understand this rationally as well. It sometimes happens, however, that while this is believed and understood by the person, unfortunately this belief and understanding does not seep into the person's heart and emotions. The result of this is that certain [untoward] events cause him to feel heartbroken and despondent, G-d forbid.

...When, however, a person works on himself, endeavoring to have his belief and understanding filter down into his emotions, this results in the realization and feeling that "All that G-d does, He does for the good"[3] — indeed, it must be so. This enables the individual to eventually be able to perceive and feel that matters are overtly and obviously good.

For since G-d rewards the individual in kind, "measure for measure," this attitude engenders G-d's revealing to all, and particularly to that individual himself, the goodness that lies concealed in the [seemingly unpleasant event,] so that it may be perceived [for the good it truly is,] even with the naked eye.

...I extend to you my prayerful wishes that very soon G-d should demonstrate to you the complete goodness that transpired in the past events in your life and which you have failed to see until now, and that you be truly joyful in all aspects, both spiritual and material.

(Igros Kodesh, Vol. IV, p. 220)

---

3   *Berachos* 60b.

DEALING WITH SETBACKS AND ADVERSITY

...I surely need not emphasize to you that a true businessman is not one who can manage his affairs when conditions are favorable and matters are running smoothly and successfully, but also, and even more so, when he demonstrates that he knows how to deal with adversity and the occasional setback.

Indeed, facing up to the challenge of adversity makes one a stronger and more effective executive than before, with an added dimension of experience and a keener acumen, which can be put to good use even when things begin to turn upwards.

Sometimes, a temporary setback is just what is needed for the resumption of the advance with greater vigor, as in the case of an athlete having to negotiate a hurdle, where stepping back is necessary in order to facilitate a higher leap.

(From a letter of the Rebbe, dated 25 Shevat, 5736)

OVERCOMING FEELINGS OF ABANDONMENT AND HAVING ONE'S LIFE DEPEND ENTIRELY UPON ONESELF

...Surely you are correct in writing that you have already suffered enough; it is high time for everyone to be helped in all that they require, particularly with regard to good health, and I hope you will be able to convey to me glad tidings regarding your improved health.

I wish to note the following, although I am not entirely

sure whether this is wholly germane to your situation:

Quite often, a person's feelings of self-assurance and security are dependent on something outside of and higher than himself — in simpler terms, [they are dependent] on his feelings of faith and *bitachon* in the Creator of the world as a whole and man's personal world in particular.

After the earthshaking events of our generation,[4] which have shaken various spiritual foundations and torn many individuals from deeply rooted family and national traditions, it affected many people and caused them to think that they were left hanging in the air; [i.e., without something to which they could anchor their lives].

I am referring here even to those of them who are believers; their faith became something that was disconnected from their practical everyday life. They would think about their faith, recite *Shema Yisrael* or *Modeh Ani*, often thinking about the meaning of the words, and yet they would go around the entire day with the thought that they were entirely alone, each of them drawing conclusions from these thoughts according to their nature and personality.

The most realistic manner of helping such individuals regain their equilibrium is by revealing within them their familial and ancestral traditions that even now remain concealed within their souls.

They will then perceive that man is not alone. Moreover, they will realize that man is the master of his lot only to a certain extent; for the most part it depends on G-d.

Consequently, the person need not place all the burden[s of his life] on his own shoulders, feeling a tremendously weighty responsibility for everything that happens to him. Surely he need

---

4   The Rebbe's letter is from 5711 (1951), soon after the Holocaust.

not be filled with despair regarding specific matters or situations.

When such individuals are connected with their fount of faith and *bitachon*, which without the slightest doubt remains deeply rooted in them, this will lead to their peace of mind and will enable them to live their lives in a healthier manner and better be able to fulfill the unique tasks that each and every individual has in life....

(Igros Kodesh, Vol. IV, p. 248)

DWELLING ON LIFE'S MISFORTUNES

...You write about the terrible decree [and misfortune] that transpired...:

Understandably, you should uproot such thoughts and those like them, since a) they are without foundation; b) there is the celebrated adage uttered by the Rebbeim and *Nesi'im* generation after generation: "Think positively, and you will see positive results;" [and] c) it is known that the crucial determinant of a person's feelings when he is unsure of their validity is to ascertain how these feelings will affect his deeds and actions.

We verily observe that the emotions you demonstrate (regarding the harshness of the decree) leads to a lessening of one's good deeds, as well as to despondency and loss of hope. These negative traits are not prohibited and eliminated only for spiritual reasons, but for simple common sense reasons as well.

In place of the above, it is my opinion that there lies a sacred *obligation* on all the friends of the family [of the deceased] to try over and over again to insure that the children of ... *alav ha-shalom* follow the path of Torah and *mitzvos* in their daily lives.

Understandably, it is specifically this that is of the greatest import — of crucial importance not only to the children of the deceased, but to the deceased himself. This is infinitely more important than eulogies or memorial services.

Surely I need not demonstrate to you the truth of such a simple matter, nor need I explain it at further length....

(Igros Kodesh, Vol. XVI, p. 213)

LEADING A PURPOSEFUL LIFE — AN ANTIDOTE TO LIFE'S CHALLENGES

...Referring to your letter and various questions and problems about which you write, I want to dwell on Item 6 of your letter, which contains the key to all the other problems. In this paragraph you mentioned that you feel depressed and cannot see any reasons for a brighter future. You ask how you can get rid of your fears.

The answer is completely simple. When a person will reflect, in a logical way about the creation and the order and precision and laws that are to be found in nature, the conclusion must be inescapable. There is a tremendous system of order in the universe, and strict laws, and, therefore there can be no doubt that the world is regulated by plan, order and purpose.

The very fact that there is order, purpose and law in the universe, must lead one to the conviction that all that is good, since evil is the opposite of order and system, and is associated with chaos.

No matter how much importance a person attaches to one's own self and one's own problems, he must recognize that if there is such order in such a complicated universe, how much easier it is to bring about law and order in one's own small universe - a thought which should lead to satisfaction and peace of mind.

If there are people who complicate their lives, it is because people have free choice of action and mind. But this very fact of the human being having a free will is part of the entire system of goodness and purpose in the world, for it was G-d's design that the human being should not be an automaton but should be able, freely, to choose eternal life and goodness.

If we consider all of the above, we must come to the firm conviction that if man would not upset his own life through circumstances depending upon his free will, he would inevitably come to the good. Even if, temporarily, one finds oneself in an unpleasant or painful situation, it is surely infinitely insignificant by comparison to all the good that will result from it.

By way of illustration: If you see a person working a job for somebody else, it would seem at first glance that the employer is exploiting the knowledge, experience and energy of the employee, and that the employee seemingly has no immediate benefit from his toil. To him who is unaware that at the end of the week the worker will receive his pay envelope, it would seem the height of cruelty and injustice to exploit another human being in this fashion. But come pay day at the end of the week, the worker will receive full compensation for his sweat and toil, which will enable him to support himself, his wife and family. It will then be clear that non only is there no injustice or cruelty in such work, but that the work is amply compensated.

Similarly, in one's personal life. If it seems to one that there appears to be no purpose in his personal life and that there seems to be, rather, more pain than pleasure in it, it is only because one cannot foresee the future and the results of the circumstances which have caused such pain and exertion.

However, the firm faith and knowledge that the Almighty is Master of the universe, and that every human being is but a small part of it, and, therefore, the Almighty is Master also of the personal life of each human being with all that happens in it, also gives the certain knowledge that no matter how one's life is shaped, there must be justice in it and each human being will, sooner or later, depending upon his merit and energy, eventually see that that is so.

In the light of the above, you may be quite certain that there is a good answer to all your problems and that eventually all the complications will be resolved satisfactorily. Needless to say, one has to seek to solve one's problems, but there can be no room for a feeling of depression and certainly no room for a feeling of despondency, which can be nothing but destructive.

With regard to Item No. 1, in which you complain about lack of good health, it is no doubt largely due to the state of nervousness and depression you are in. I am sure that if you will try to correct this, which depends entirely on you, you will also find a considerable improvement in your health, and you will also be able to respond much better to the treatments which specialists give you.

The same applies to Items No. 2, 3 and 4. If you will develop a more optimistic view on life it will give you a more cheerful disposition, your job will not appear so difficult and tedious, and you will not feel so unhappy about it. This will also help you to get your suitable match in due course.

With regard to Item No. 5, concerning the *"Ayin Hara"* the best thing is to dismiss it from your mind and give a few cents every morning for *Tzedakah* before the prayer of Shema.

Item Np. 7, regarding psychiatric help. If you mean seeking psychiatric advice through a visit or two, and the psychiatrist in question is one who understands the atmosphere in the Jewish religious home, there can be no objection to it. However, I would not recommend that you undertake lengthy psychiatric treatment, since you yourself could do considerably more for yourself than any psychiatrist can do for you.

I have turned over your contribution to our Special Charity Fund, from which help is given anonymously to deserving cases, which is one of the highest forms of *Tzedakah*, and I trust that it will add to your merits to become one who is happy with his lot and soon to see with your own eyes that you have good reasons to be happy.

With prayerful wishes and blessings,

(From a letter of the Rebbe, dated 8 Cheshvan, 5713)

RECOGNIZING THE GOOD IN LIFE

From time to time I inquire about your wellbeing and receive news about your welfare from your children *sheyichyu.* I am surprised by the fact that on a number of occasions they have told me that your mood is not as it should be.

In general, each and every one of us, when we search and ponder our lives, even during the last few years [when matters do not seem to be going so well,] will observe G-d's kindness [and goodness], up to and including matters that were not at all expected.

In fact, the individual sees these things to an even greater extent than does another — as each person knows in his or her own life.

This should lead the person to recognize and acknowledge the blessings [and goodness] that he has received from G-d, and quite possibly, on more than one occasion, the person has received these blessings without any effort on his part.

This leads to the inevitable conclusion that if there do exist matters that are contrary to a person's desires, then [it may very well be one of two things]:

Firstly, quite often a person does not truly know what is best for him and if that which he desires will indeed bring him true benefit or possibly the opposite.

Even when the individual concludes that he knows with one-hundred-percent certainty that the thing is good for him, he still cannot possibly know the reasons he has not been granted these matters for the time being.

This is analogous to the business world: A good and experienced businessperson will not sell his merchandise at an inopportune time. This is the case even when he can realize a profit, but that he reckons that by selling his merchandise at a later date he can realize a *far greater* profit.

The same is so with G-d's goodness. If it is delayed, it is likely because at a later time G-d's beneficence will be in a much greater manner in both quantity and quality.

This is particularly true in your case, where G-d has blessed you with true *nachas* from children, something which is not so often found.... Since you and your wife *tichye* can anticipate even more *nachas* [from your children,] your going around unhappy (something which can be interpreted as dissatisfaction — G-d forbid — with the manner in which G-d conducts your affairs) defies understanding. Moreover, to a certain extent this is an expression of ingratitude to G-d.

It is self-understood that I am not writing to you in order to admonish you, but to convince you that even according to the way you look at your life, the good things in your life are incomparably greater and more significant than those matters that you think are — temporarily — not as they should be.

[Bear in mind] that when a businessman makes an accounting, he does not consider each item individually, but makes a total accounting of the inventory. [And so too regarding the "balance sheet" of events in your life.]

It is my hope that the above few lines will move you to reconsider the "calculation" that you are making. I am sure that when you do so, you will reach a much happier conclusion [than you have reached until now]....

(Igros Kodesh, Vol. XIII, p. 249)

EXPERIENCING GOODNESS THROUGHOUT ONE'S LIFE

I was astounded to read in the letter that I received from you that your husband *sheyichye's* spirits are very low.

How can this possibly be after the two of you have personally witnessed and experienced G-d's wonders and kindnesses? This [experience] should rouse you to great joy, for "In the shining countenance of a king" — the King of kings, blessed G-d — "there is life."[5]

And yet, notwithstanding the above, to find oneself in a depressed state?! Surely this is nothing but the machinations of the evil inclination. It is my strong hope that this [low mood] is but a temporary phenomenon, and that it has already passed.

Moreover, we have been promised and assured by our sacred Torah, the Torah of Life, that whenever one has been shown kindness and goodness from Above, it is for many long and good years.

Surely this promise will be fulfilled with regard to you and your husband as well. I await very speedily glad tidings with regard to the above.

(Igros Kodesh, Vol. XIV, p. 410)

DO NOT BECOME CRESTFALLEN BY LIFE'S CHALLENGES

...Surely I need not explain at length to an individual like yourself that there is no room for feeling downhearted from your encountering some difficulties in the course of fulfilling your true task in life, that of "I was created to serve my Maker."

Such feelings are from the machinations of the evil inclination that seeks to bring the person to a crestfallen state. In point of fact, the entire purpose of the evil inclination lies in man's vanquishing it. {Indeed, this, [i.e., that the evil inclination be vanquished,] is also the desire of the evil inclination [itself], as is to be understood from the holy *Zohar*, quoted in *Tanya* at the conclusion of ch. 29.}

---

5   *Mishlei* 16:15.

Ultimately, even those matters that presently conceal and obscure [goodness and holiness] are themselves transformed into good — and not only in a manner of "All that G-d does, He does for the good," i.e., that goodness will eventually result, but in a manner of "This too is for the good," i.e., that the matter itself becomes good.

{This difference is to be understood from the story itself of *Nachum Ish Gam Zu*, wherein the transformation of the earth [into weapons] served as overtly revealed goodness, as opposed to the expression "All that G-d does, He does for the good," [wherein it was merely "for the good" but it was not transformed into actual goodness.]}

This is particularly so as we are now commencing the days of the month in which there is the [joyous] festival of Purim, about which our holy Torah states: "The month" — i.e., this is true of the entire month — "that was transformed for the Jews into [a month of] joy and *Yom Tov.*"

Now, the concept of "transformation" [during this month] means that the entire month is propitious for transforming those [untoward] events into a form of "joy and *Yom Tov*" that is palpably revealed to us.

(Igros Kodesh, Vol. XIV, p. 441)

OUR CHALLENGES ARE COMMENSURATE WITH OUR ABILITIES

It saddened me to learn that your health is not as it should be. Surely a large part is merely nerves and imagination, as well as the fact of not serving G-d with joy, which according to the ruling of the *Rambam* — quoted in the *Tur* and *Shulchan Aruch, Orach Chayim*, ch. 231, and in many other places — includes all aspects of a Jew's life, including eating, drinking, etc.

Frankly, I am surprised ... for proper faith in G-d compels one to conclude, "a camel is only loaded according to its ability to bear [the load]";[6] i.e., G-d does not demand of a person Divine service that is beyond his capacity. Since "maintaining a healthy and robust body is an integral part of Divine service," surely this service does not in and of itself diminish the person's health.

The fact at times there are obstacles and difficulties, and at times it seems — and is possibly quite true — that the obstacles and difficulties are abundant.

Nevertheless, of that which is explained in *Tanya*[7] on the verse ["And make me] delicacies [such as I love],"[8] it is known that the term "delicacies" is written in the plural, for there are two forms of "delicacies" and "delights" that one can give G-d — spiritual service that does not require battling evil and service that does require a battle.

However, even in the latter instance, one goes to battle with a joyous march, as known from the *sichah* of my father-in-law, the Rebbe.

Thus regarding spiritual service that requires a battle — [it is to be done with joy] and it should not affect one's health, although it should be a matter of concern....

(Igros Kodesh, Vol. XIX, p. 413)

---

6   *Kesuvos* 67a.

7   Ch. 27.

8   *Bereishis* 27:4.

EVEN AFTER TRUE TRAGEDY STRIKES ONE SHOULD COMBAT DOWNHEARTEDNESS

It pained me to learn that you are still in a downhearted mood, and according to my understanding this is the mood in your household as well.

I don't want to go on at length and enter into a debate as to whether your attitude is correct or not. Understandably, it does not take much contemplation to appreciate why you are all in such a frame of mind after the tragedy that occurred — may we all never know of such events again.

The above notwithstanding, Jews in general and chassidim in particular as "believers" are expected to unequivocally cleave to G-d, keeping their relationship with Him open, as the verse states,[9] "And you who cleave to the L-rd your G-d are all alive today."

Life, true life, does not mean simply marking time, it means that one's life lacks for nothing, with both the person and his family possessing all their spiritual and material needs.

Since the possibility exists that — G-d forbid — they have not earned this generous bounty from G-d, therefore the holy *Zohar* (II, p. 184b) tenders the advice: "They [— this physical world and man in general —] exist by the 'radiant countenance' [i.e., the joy and positivity,] that is emitted from below. In a like manner they then draw down upon themselves the same qualities from Above. Man's joy draws down a corresponding measure of joy from Above."

Concisely stated: When one strengthens himself in his *bitachon* in G-d that He will surely provide those matters with

---

9   *Devarim* 4:4.

which a person can be in good spirits, happy and joyous, doing so in such a powerful manner that his *bitachon* affects his daily life, then one draws down this Divine beneficence from Above. One then verily sees that his *bitachon* was justified.

May G-d help that you, your wife, and your entire family experience this as quickly as possible and in as discernible a manner as possible.

(Igros Kodesh, Vol. VI, p. 266)

OVERCOMING LIFE'S ADVERSITIES

I am in receipt of your letter in which you write about various recent events in your life — which were not in the category of obvious good — and you ask what your reaction should be.

In general, as you surely know, Jews are guided by the Torah, the "Torah of Life," which is to say that Torah is the Jew's true guide in everyday life. The Torah is also called *Torah Or*, the "Torah of Illumination," since it illuminates the Jew's life and its instructions are as clear and lucid as light itself.

One of the best-known portions of the Torah, which Jews recite daily in both morning and evening, is the portion of the *Shema*, in which the Torah tells us to love G-d "with all your heart and with all your soul and with all your might."

The Hebrew word *m'odecha*, generally translated as "your might," also conveys the meaning of *middah* — "measure" or "dimension," as our Sages explain. This means that a Jew has to love G-d regardless of the kind of "deal" he thinks is meted out to him by Divine providence.

This profound love is to express itself, as the text indicates, in the study of Torah and the observance of its *mitzvos*, particularly the *mitzvos* of *tefillin* and *mezuzah* which are mentioned specifically, and particularly so since *tefillin* is symbolic of all the *mitzvos*.

Moreover, inasmuch as [the hand] *tefillin* is placed on the left arm facing the heart, the seat of the emotions, and [the head *tefillin*] on the head facing the brain, the seat of the intellect, *tefillin* symbolizes that a Jew is to be totally involved — both emotionally and intellectually — in serving and fulfilling His commandments.

In other words, whatever happens in a Jew's life must not in any way affect his love of and devotion to G-d, nor his everyday life and conduct in accordance with the Torah and *mitzvos*. (Needless to say, the *mitzvah* of reciting the *Shema* daily is not reserved for exceptional Jews, but is for each and every Jew.)

The question now arises: Is the above something that can really be implemented, and if so, how is one to explain how this can actually be implemented?

To be sure, the human intellect is limited and cannot possibly fathom the Divine wisdom that is in the Torah. On the other hand, the Torah itself describes the Jewish people as a "wise and understanding people," and it provides at least some explanation that helps us to understand, in however limited a degree, G-d's ways.

One of the basic teachings of the Torah is that G-d does not expect anything of a human being that is beyond the human capacity to carry out.

This, in fact, is eminently understandable: Even a human being, who is a very long way away from absolute perfection, would not expect a tool that he has fashioned to perform in a capacity greater than its original design. Certainly G-d, the

Creator of man, knows man's capacities.

From this it naturally follows that when a Jew faces any kind of a test of faith, it is certain that he has been given the capacity to overcome it. And the more difficult the test, the greater are the individual's capacities.

The reason that an individual is tested is not that G-d wants to know how well he will conduct himself, but in order that this person be afforded the opportunity to realize his potential, even that which is unknown to him. And when one's potential capacities are released and activated, they become part and parcel of his or her arsenal, to be used for personal as well as communal benefit....

(From a letter of the Rebbe)

SETTING LIMITS TO LEGITIMATE SORROW AND GRIEVING

I have just received your letter of the 3rd of *Tammuz*.

To begin with a blessing, may G-d grant that henceforth you and all your family receive only goodness and benevolence — overtly revealed goodness.

At the same time, despite your [understandable] pain, you must make every effort to regain your former equilibrium.

You should remember the teaching and instruction of the Torah, which is called *Toras Chayim*, the "Guide to Life," and *Toras Emes*, the "Torah of Truth," meaning that what it teaches is not just to ease the mind, but is the actual truth.

Taking into account human nature and feelings in a condition and state of bereavement, and recognizing the need to provide an outlet for the natural feelings of sorrow and grief, the Torah prescribes a set of regulations and periods of mourning.

At the same time, the Torah sets limits in terms of the duration of the periods of mourning and their appropriate expression, such as *shivah* [the first seven days], *shloshim* [the first thirty days], etc.

If one extends the intensity of mourning which is appropriate for *shivah* into *shloshim*, it is not proper, for although *shloshim* is part of the overall mourning period, it is so to a lesser degree.

Since the Torah states that it is not proper to overdo it, excessive grieving does no good for the *neshamah* [the soul] of the dear departed. On the contrary, it is painful for the *neshamah* to see that it is the cause of conduct that is not in keeping with the Torah's instructions.

A second point to bear in mind is that a human being cannot possibly understand the ways of G-d. By way of a simple illustration:

An infant cannot possibly understand the thinking and conduct of a great scholar or scientist — even though both are human beings and the difference between them is only relative in terms of age, education and maturity. This is so notwithstanding the fact that quite possibly at some future date the infant may even surpass the scientist, who also began his life as an infant.

The difference, however, between a created human being and his Creator is absolute. Therefore, our Sages declare that human beings must accept everything that happens — both those matters that are obviously good as well as those matters wherein the goodness is humanly incomprehensible — since "All that G-d does, He does for the good."[10]

---

10   *Berachos* 60b.

Nevertheless, G-d enabled us to grasp some aspects and insights regarding life in this world and the afterlife. One of these insights is that the *neshamah* is a part of G-dliness and as such is immortal. When the time comes for it to return to Heaven, it leaves the body and continues its eternal life in the spiritual World of Truth.

It is also a matter of common sense that whatever precisely caused the separation of the soul from the body (whether a fatal accident or a fatal illness, etc.), its effect was only on the vital organs of the physical body. In no way did it affect the spiritual soul.

A further point, which can also be understood: During the soul's lifetime on earth, which it lived in partnership with the body, the soul was necessarily "handicapped" — in certain respects — by the physical requirements of the body (such as eating and drinking, etc.).

Even a *tzaddik* (a wholly righteous individual), whose entire life is consecrated to G-d, cannot escape the constraints of living his life in a material and physical environment. Consequently, when the time comes for the soul to return "home," it is essentially a release for it as it makes its ascent to a higher world, no longer [spiritually restricted and] restrained by a physical body and environment. From now on, the soul is free to enjoy the spiritual bliss of being close to G-d to the fullest extent. That is surely a comforting thought.

It may be asked, if it is a "release" for the soul, why has the Torah prescribed periods of mourning, etc.? But there is really no contradiction.

The Torah recognizes the natural feeling of grief that is felt by the loss of a near and dear one, whose passing leaves a void in the family; the physical presence and contact of the beloved one will be sorely missed.

So the Torah has prescribed the proper periods of mourning to give vent to these feelings and make it easier to regain the proper equilibrium and balance.

However, allowing oneself to be carried away by these feelings beyond the limits set by the Torah — in addition to it being a disservice to oneself and those around him, as well as to the soul as mentioned above — means that the individual is more concerned with his own feelings than with the feelings of the precious *neshamah* that has risen to new spiritual heights of eternal bliss.

Thus, paradoxically, an overextended feeling of grief, which is a result of the great love for the departed one, actually causes pain to the loved one, since the *neshamah* continues to take an interest in the dear ones left behind, is aware of what is going on (to an even greater extent than before), rejoices with them in their joys, etc.

One thing the departed soul can no longer do is the actual fulfillment of the *mitzvos*, which can only be carried out when the soul and body are joined together in this material world. But this, too, can at least partly be overcome when those left behind do a little more in the area of *mitzvos* and good deeds — in honor and for the benefit of the dear departed *neshamah*.

More could be said on the subject, but I trust the above will suffice to help you discover within yourself the strength that G-d has given you, not only to overcome this crisis, but also to go from strength to strength in your everyday life and activities in full accord with the Torah....

(From a letter of the Rebbe, dated 5 Tammuz, 5743)

DEALING WITH LIFE'S TRAGIC AND INEXPLICABLE EVENTS

...In answer to your question concerning the [tragic] events that recently occurred in your family; that you find them incomprehensible and inexplicable [and they are distressing and unsettling you]:

As already mentioned on a number of occasions, it is not at all surprising when man cannot comprehend the conduct of G-d; to the contrary, it would be truly astonishing if we could understand G-d's conduct.

Concerning this matter there is the familiar analogy of a child who is in kindergarten and is unable to comprehend the rules and principles by which the country is governed, or the rulings of the Supreme Court. Even if the kindergarten-er were to be a true child genius, his limited comprehension would make him incapable of understanding the above rules and principles.

This is so notwithstanding the fact that the leaders of the land and the members of the court were also once of kindergarten age, and with time this child may attain a degree of knowledge that will surpass these leaders and jurists.

How, then, can we possibly compare a human's comprehension with G-d's, claiming that man's intellect be capable of understanding the conduct of the Creator of the world, the Supreme Ruler over everyone and everything. I trust that I need not add anything more to the above.

There are only a small number of matters that G-d wanted [to be known] and revealed, and those matters were presented by Him in a manner that human intellect would be fully capable of discerning and comprehending.

Another point needs to be stated: The more a person relies on his pure faith and *bitachon* in G-d, the more he will see and logically comprehend the events that transpire in the world as a whole and in one's private life in particular.

May G-d bless you in all matters that you require, among the most important of them true serenity and peace of mind. May He bless you that your life be such that matters will be good for you in all aspects, including goodness that is overtly revealed and intellectually comprehensible.

Your daily conduct in accordance with our holy Torah, which is called "*Toras Chayim*," a living Torah that shows how to live, is the manner and vessel to receive these blessings from G-d.

(Igros Kodesh, Vol. XXIV, p. 111)

DISPOSE OF THE NEGATIVE ATTITUDE

In reply to your letter of 12/13 in which you describe the various circumstances that you and your husband *sheyichye* have experienced: You reach the conclusion that things were always not well and now things are also not fine, etc. — from which we can easily discern your view regarding what the future holds in store for you:

I am astonished by your conclusions, when you yourself write that from the entire family you were among the few survivors; you also write about the various maladies and ailments that you survived; you also write about your husband that one could never imagine ... and he nevertheless occupied himself [and succeeded] in matters; that you both find yourselves in a house, etc.

Recognizing all the above, being cognizant of all that transpired not only externally but in the house as well, how is it possible to conclude in the manner that you write?!

Of course one should ask G-d that things become better and better, for G-d is the "Essence of Goodness" and "It is the nature of He who is good to do good." However, one should not ignore the many kindnesses of G-d that one has already experienced — particularly as you write that you perceived openly revealed kindnesses and miracles.

I wish to reiterate: My intent is not to minimize the importance of being aware of one's needs, and I also don't mean to imply that you are not lacking necessities. I merely wish to accentuate the goodness — indeed the very large amount of goodness — which you and your husband perceived with your physical eyes.

Another point (and this is of equal importance):

Our holy Torah explains that the measure of G-d's blessings depends to a considerable extent on the [appreciative] manner in which the person receives these blessings, and that his conduct is in consonance with and in recognition of these kindnesses. This form of behavior enlarges the receptacles and vessels that allow one to receive His kindnesses in the immediate future, as well as in the future in general....

(Igros Kodesh, Vol. XVIII, p. 137)

chapter 2

COMBATING SADNESS, DESPONDENCY, DEPRESSION AND DESPAIR

DESPONDENCY AND DEPRESSION

...Bear in mind the following points:

(a) There can be no question that *teshuvah*, penitence, is effective in every case, whatever the transgression, for *teshuvah* is one of G-d's commandments, and G-d does not require of us the impossible.

(b) It is likewise certain that any kind of depression, despondency or sadness [as a result of agonizing over past sins] is a trick of the *yetzer hara*, the evil inclination, to discourage one from serving G-d....

I advise you from now on to stop weighing and dwelling on things that are of no practical value, and especially the kinds of thoughts that only lead to despondency; rather place ever-increasing efforts on the performance of Torah and *mitzvos*....

(From a letter of the Rebbe, dated Erev Shavuos, 5716)

COMBATING SADNESS

...With regard to your inclination towards a feeling of sadness:

A useful remedy for this is to have firmly engraved in your mind that G-d, the Creator of the world, watches over everyone individually.

Since He is the Essence of Goodness, there is therefore no room for sadness or worry; this [concept] has been explained at length in various parts of the *Tanya* (see Index [at the back of the *Tanya*]).

It would be especially good for you to commit to memory the passage of *Tanya* at the beginning of chapter 41 (p. 56a), second line from the bottom. Whenever you feel sad or depressed, review that section in your mind or recite it orally. This will assist you in eliminating these undesirable emotions.

(From a letter of the Rebbe, dated 7 Adar, 5717)

THREE FORMS OF REALITY

...You write in your letter about your [depressed] state of mind.

As known, there are many matters that exist wholly outside the person; other [mental health] issues [such as neuroses and psychoses] that at least exist within the individual's inner [sense of reality and] self; and finally, there are those matters whose entire existence [and reality] is a result of the person's thinking about them.

Although it would seem that when thinking about a certain thing [whose entire existence is predicated on his thoughts about the matter], there is no difference whether or not his thoughts refer to a factual reality, but in truth this is not so: there always exists within the individual the ability to examine his feelings and their degree of authenticity and certitude.

This assessment affects the person even when his capacity to make a "reality check" is concealed, or to use the common vernacular, lies within his subconscious, which can then be recovered.

Clearly, the thoughts and feelings that you are now experiencing emanate from the latter [of the three forms of reality: they only exist because you insist on thinking about them].

Such types of thoughts and feelings are much easier [to get rid of]; quite often they dissipate on their own by simply ceasing to think these thoughts — either a cessation resulting from an external factor [such as through an intervention by another person], or brought about by the person's own resolve to stop thinking about them.

...We verily observe that hundreds and thousands of people who found themselves in the same frame of mind as you do now were able to rid themselves of these feelings without it having any lasting effect on them at all (from which we understand that this can ultimately be achieved even by those who still retain some vestige of these feelings).

[These statistics may not be so well known,] merely because it is human nature to greatly publicize those matters that are entirely in the minority, or those matters that are truly uncommon, [i.e., individuals whose feelings of gloominess overwhelm them,] while the more common experience [of people gaining control of their feelings] is not publicized at all.

...Thus, with even minor reflection we realize that it is incumbent on each and every one of us to fulfill our mission in this world; i.e., to increase luminosity within the world and particularly within our own environs, by strengthening and disseminating the light of life in consonance with the directives of our Torah, the Torah of Life.

Since this is the case, we do not even have the luxury of

the available time that it takes to contemplate thoughts about ourselves, i.e., thoughts of the type that you have been having.

And although at the beginning it is not easy to replace thoughts concerning ourselves with thoughts concerning our purpose in G-d's world, with time and practice it becomes easier to switch our thoughts — particularly so, when we do all the above with joy, the foundation of this joy being that which the *Rambam* writes at the conclusion of *Hilchos Lulav*, [concerning the vital importance of serving G-d joyfully]....

(Igros Kodesh, Vol. XIV, p. 22)

COMBATING DEPRESSION

...You write that you feel depressed, as it seems to you that you have not succeeded in your studies at the *Yeshivah* to the extent that you expected. Even assuming that you are completely correct in your appraisal, this would still be no reason for feeling depressed.

For, as it is explained in many sources, especially *Tanya*, even in the case of spiritual failure, no Jew should feel depressed, for a feeling of depression and gloom is, in itself, one of the strategic weapons used by the *yetzer hara* in an effort to discourage a person from serving G-d with joy and alacrity.

And when the *yetzer hara* succeeds in one thing, such as in discouraging you from studying, as you write, he goes on to further things.

The way to combat the *yetzer hara* is, as explained in *Tanya*, to call forth a redoubled effort on your part to overcome the feeling of depression, replacing it with a feeling of joy. You can accomplish this by recognizing that whatever one's past has been, it is still always possible to attach oneself to G-d through the study of the Torah and the observance of the *mitzvos*.

In the case of persistent distraction, the well-known illustration used in the *Tanya* is to imagine that a heathen is standing nearby while one is in the midst of prayer and trying to distract one from concentrating on prayer and study.

In such a case, one would certainly not blame himself [for becoming distracted]. Rather, one would redouble his efforts to concentrate on his prayer or study, completely ignoring the outside distractions.

Thus, in the final analysis, it is up to a person to overcome his difficulties by his own efforts and determination, and we have already been assured that where there is a determined effort, success is certain.

Moreover, it is quite possible in your case that you have truly underestimated your success, and your belief to the contrary, [i.e., that you have not succeeded,] is merely a result of a thought implanted in your mind by the *yetzer hara* [in order to succeed in making you feel glum and downhearted]....

(From a letter of the Rebbe, dated 25 Menachem Av, 5718)

TRADITIONAL AND OBSERVABLE VIEW OF MELANCHOLY AND DEPRESSION

In reply to your letter of *Motzaei Shabbos:* There is surely no need to alert you to the fact that the sages and luminaries of Israel held melancholy and gloominess in *extreme* disfavor. This is also discussed in *Tanya,* ch. 26, and in many other places.

In addition, one can plainly observe that not only does such an attitude fail to correct any situation, but in fact it does quite the opposite.

This is also true regarding the matters with which you are occupied. It is especially true in this country where a happy approach strikes a responsive chord in people's hearts, whereas its opposite does not....

(Igros Kodesh, Vol. X, p. 258)

FEELINGS OF DISSATISFACTION AND DESPONDENCY

...Leaving the details of your complaints aside, I wish to make several observations:

1. Feeling dissatisfied with oneself is a good sign, for it indicates vitality and an urge to rise and improve oneself, which is accomplished via a two-way method: withdrawal from the present state, and turning to a higher level (see *sichah* of my father-in-law, the Rebbe, of sainted memory, Pesach 5694).

2. If the urge to improve oneself leads to downheartedness and inertia, then it is the work of the *yetzer hara,* whose job it is to use every means at its disposal to prevent a Jew from carrying out good intentions connected with Torah and *mitzvos.*

The false and misleading voice of the *yetzer hara* should be stifled and ignored. Besides, as the Alter Rebbe states (*Tanya,* ch. 25), even one single good deed creates an *everlasting* bond and communion with G-d (*ibid.,* at length).

Thus a feeling of despondency is not only out of place, it is a stumbling block to the worship of G-d, as is more fully explained in the above and subsequent chapters of *Tanya*....

(From a letter of the Rebbe, dated 16 Adar, 5712)

BITTERNESS AND MELANCHOLY STEMMING FROM THE "OTHER SIDE"

Your letter of 25 *Iyar* just reached me. No doubt you have long since received the booklet and the *sichah* together with my letter, and at auspicious times I mention your name and your wife's name at the holy resting place of my revered father-in-law with reference to your needs.

As I wrote you long ago, I have one thing to say: I do not understand your bitterness and melancholy at all. Since[1] "even the caretaker of a well is appointed in Heaven," and this certainly applies in regards to a rabbi of a Jewish community, you should be aware of the responsibility that rests upon you. It is even more obvious that if notions such as those [of which you write] bring you to bitterness and melancholy, they certainly stem from "the Other Side"[2] — or, to borrow the phrase of my revered father-in-law, "the cunning one."[3] Accordingly, every time and every moment that you think such thoughts, these thoughts emanate

---

1   *Bava Kamma* 27b.

2   In the original Aramaic, *sitra dile'umas zeh* (from *Koheles* 7:14: "G-d created this [side] opposite that [side]"): the evil counterpart to the aspect of holiness in the universe; a chassidic euphemism for the forces of evil.

3   In the original Yiddish, *dem kluginken.*

from the chambers of "the Other Side" — and concerning a thought of this kind it is written[4] that "as soon as it rises there (i.e., to one's mind), one thrusts it aside with both hands and averts his mind from it [...], and refuses to accept it."

Now, this is speaking of every man, for[5] "the rank of *Beinoni* is one that is attainable by every man, and every man should strive after it." (This is not contradicted by the statement in *Tanya*[6] that the *Beinoni* "has never committed any transgression," whereas chapter 14 states that "every person can, at any time or hour, be a *Beinoni.*" The meaning [of the former statement] is that the *Beinoni's* present spiritual state is such that transgressing has no place in his life, neither in the future nor in the past.[7] This will suffice for now.)

From all the above, it will be clear that I am not at all comfortable to read in your letter that you are seeking a different position. You should remain in your present post and trust firmly that G-d will lead you in the path of truth[8] and bless your holy work with success. If doubts about this enter your mind, this does not indicate a doubt in your ability, but a weakness in your trust. The remedy for this is to study *Shaar HaBitachon* in *Chovos HaLevavos,*[9] and, more broadly, to be bound to the Tree of Life, i.e., the study of *Chassidus,* and to participate frequently in chassidic *farbrengens* with genuine chassidic joy — to be happy and to make others happy.

Now, since you have moved into your new apartment, the

---

4   *Tanya,* ch. 12 (see *Lessons In Tanya* [Kehot, NY, 5742/1982], Vol. 1, p. 182).

5   *Op. cit.,* ch. 14 (see *Lessons In Tanya,* Vol. 1, p. 203).

6   Ch. 12 (see *op. cit.,* pp. 170-171).

7   I.e., from the perspective of his present state he has never sinned.

8   Cf. *Bereishis* 24:48.

9   Medieval classic (in Eng. translation: *Duties of the Heart*) by Rabbeinu Bachaye.

thing to do would be to organize a chassidic *farbrengen* there, truly and properly, and remind yourself of the good old days, when a chassid at a *farbrengen* would speak [candidly], without hesitating to consider what this one or that one would say, or what his own left side or right side[10] would say. A chassid only knew that a chassidic *farbrengen* — listening to a discourse of *Chassidus,* a chassidic *vort,*[11] or an anecdote about one of our Rebbeim — brings in light, and[12] "a little light dispels a great deal of darkness."

Furthermore: Why should one think about darkness? Let's think more about light — especially now, when we are at the time at which the First Tablets of the law were given.[13] And, [interpreting] the phrase[14] "engraved *(charus)* on the Tablets" [on the non-literal level called *derush*], the Sages taught:[15] "Do not read *charus* ('engraved'); read *cheirus* ('freedom')."[16]

May it be G-d's will that your new apartment exemplify the adage[17] that "he who changes his place changes his fortune" — in a good direction. May your home be a warm home and a happy home, filled with[18] "a commandment, [which] is a lamp, and the Torah, [which] is light." May it be filled with the luminary within the Torah, i.e., the teachings of *Chassidus,* and the spiritual lifestyle of *Chassidus,* and the customs of

---

10 I.e., his own evil inclination or good inclination, respectively (see *Tanya,* ch. 9).

11 Lit., "word" (Yid.): a teaching that is brief, quotable and insightful.

12 *Tzeidah LaDerech,* ch. 12.

13 This letter is dated two days after Shavuos.

14 *Shmos* 32:16.

15 *Avos* 6:2.

16 I.e., studying Torah liberates a man.

17 In the original, *"Meshaneh makom meshaneh mazal";* cf. *Rosh HaShanah* 16b.

18 *Mishlei* 6:23.

chassidim. And you should hold a chassidic *farbrengen* there from time to time.

I look forward to hearing glad tidings regarding an improvement in your frame of mind, and to hearing that at long last — even if only as an [unenthused] assumption of responsibility[19] — you have undertaken that henceforth you will fulfill the Torah's command that one should serve G-d "with joy and with gladness of heart."[20]

(Igros Kodesh, Vol. IV, p. 318)

COMBATING DESPONDENCY THROUGH THINKING POSITIVELY

I am astounded by the fact that time and again a theme is accentuated, but when it comes to actualizing it, each and every individual tends to think that the point was made regarding someone else — not himself!

The aphorism and *directive* of our Rebbeim-*Nesi'im*, "Think positively, and you will see positive results" (the intent of which is that such positive thoughts will actually bring about good results), has been cited in numerous places.

Yet, contrary to this, you concoct entirely opposite types of thoughts, and notwithstanding the fact that we find ourselves in the month of *Adar*, at which time we are commanded to increase our joy, you wallow in despondency (see *Tanya* regarding [the inappropriateness of] this matter; [i.e., the state of despondency]).

---

19   In the original, *b'kabbalas ol.*

20   *Devarim* 28:47.

I conclude with "words of, [i.e., uttered by,] royalty," [i.e., the Rebbeim, the *Nesi'im*]: "Think positively, and you will see positive results" — clearly and conspicuously.

(Igros Kodesh, Vol. XX, p. 195)

NEGATIVE ASPECTS OF SADNESS, DEPRESSION AND DESPONDENCY

The negative aspects of all forms of sadness, depression, despondency, etc., are explained in many places in *Chassidus*, beginning with the *Tanya*.

It is also clear from experience that these attitudes belong to the bag of tricks used by the *yetzer hara* in order to distract a Jew from serving G-d. To achieve this end, the *yetzer hara* sometimes even clothes itself in a mantle of piety.

On the other hand, we have been assured that "He who is determined to purify himself receives Divine help."[21] The road to purity and holiness, however, is one that should be trodden step by step, and by gradual and steady advancement.

(From a letter of the Rebbe, dated 27 Teves, 5721)

MOST DEFINITELY DO NOT BE HEARTBROKEN

I received your telegram and letter about your safe return, and I was happy that — thank G-d — your journey went

---

21   *Yoma* 38b.

well and upon your return you found everything in order. However, it pained me how evident it was to see from your letter that you are brokenhearted [about the state of your husband's health as well as your own] — a heartbrokenness that is entirely out of place.

Surely I need not explain at length that the phrase[22] "the offering [desirable] to G-d is a broken spirit" does not refer to being brokenspirited and surely not brokenhearted — something that is detrimental, G-d forbid, to one's health and has a deleterious effect on one's nerves. Moreover, brokenheartedness leads to viewing matters in a much more pessimistic and grim light than the way the matters truly are....

(Igros Kodesh, Vol. IV, p. 340)

A "SHOT IN THE ARM" AGAINST DESPONDENCY

A hypodermic needle draws blood for the purpose of diagnosis and treatment. However, it is not the needle that draws the blood from the veins. Rather it is the vacuum in the syringe.

The lesson of the value of a vacuum can be extremely relevant to a person who considers himself "vacant" — unworthy — to be successful in his G-dly service.

An empty vessel can absorb with greater intensity than one that is full. So too can the person who is aware of his own inadequacy be more strongly motivated to study and do positive things.

---

22   *Tehillim* 51:19.

Similarly, when we find ourselves in a situation where an absence or loss is deeply felt, one need not be despondent. We can rather use the emptiness itself as an impetus for even greater achievement.

(Adapted from a sichah of the Rebbe, Simchas Torah, 5738)

NEGATION OF DEJECTION AND DESPAIR

...Regarding the content of your letter, a letter filled with dejection and despair:

This [negative attitude] is not at all in keeping with the path formulated by the Baal Shem Tov, his disciples, and his disciples' disciples, the luminaries of *Chassidus*, who stressed time and time again the Divine command to "Serve G-d with joy."

I have already written to many of *Anash*, [our chassidic brotherhood], and if memory serves me, to you as well, that conducting oneself in this [joyous] manner is an actual law and not just a meritorious manner of conduct (*middas Chassidus*). Moreover, this is a fundamental and crucial [all-embracing] commandment — not merely a limited individual specific command.

This ruling [of serving G-d with joy] is stated in the *Rambam* at the conclusion of *Hilchos Lulav*; see his [exact] wording there, [where he states:] "It is a great form of service."

In conjunction with the above, there is also *Rambam's* ruling at the conclusion of the third chapter in *Hilchos Deos* — quoted as well in the *Tur, Shulchan Aruch Orach Chayim,* chapter 231 — [where he states that when one serves G-d with joy] "...it thus results in the person constantly serving G-d ... 'knowing Him in all your ways'"; [i.e., *all* the person's activities become part of his Divine service].

Even if contemplating your situation leads you to wonder as to where there is room for joy in your life, the answer to this [question of what there is to be joyful about] is already offered by the Alter Rebbe in his sacred work of *Tanya*, [where he describes] the joy of the soul and reasons for this joy, and how, [notwithstanding bodily tribulations,] the body and its bodily affairs cannot impede on this joy — see there.[23]

May G-d will it that by return mail you convey to me glad tidings with regard to the above, and also that you are increasing your studies in [*Chassidus*,] the portion of Torah known as the "Tree of Life," where life and joy unite with each other until they become wholly integrated and truly one.

(Igros Kodesh, Vol. XV, p. 232)

EMPOWERED BY THE REBBE'S BLESSINGS

In reply to your express letter:

I have already advised — and even warned — you a number of times not to be sad and depressed, [but to be happy and joyful]. I offered you further reasoning [that you be joyful and not sad], by reminding you that my father-in-law, the Rebbe, of blessed memory הכ"מ blessed you many times — and, as the ruling in the *Talmud* states: "A *tzaddik* decrees and G-d fulfills [the *tzaddik's* decree]."

___

23   Ch. 31.

Heaven forbid that you should cast even a shadow of a doubt on [the magnitude and power of these blessings,] or that you weaken your sense of faith and trust in G-d [by placing yourself in a sad and depressed frame of mind. Such behavior] is contrary to the many sayings and aphorisms of our Sages, of blessed memory, who decried such a [self-generated] state [of sadness and depression].

Aside from the above, such behavior also damages the [spiritual] channels [through which the Divine blessings flow from Above. Proof can be adduced from the following] text of the *Zohar, Parshas Tetzaveh*, p. 184b:

"Behold, the lower world, [i.e., this physical world,] exists in a state of constant readiness to receive [the Divine flow from Above]. It is called a "precious stone." The upper world will only bestow to the lower world in accordance with [the lower world's] state and condition.

"If the lower world is in a [positive] state of luster and radiance, it will accordingly receive kindnesses from Above; if it is in a state of gloominess, then it receives 'severities' from Above.

"Therefore the verse (*Tehillim* 100:2) exhorts us: 'Serve G-d with joy.' For man's joy [in the lower world] draws down for him an even greater and more enhanced measure of joy from Above."

It is already high time that you begin complying with the above.

With blessings for goodness in all matters, especially a speedy recovery.

(Igros Kodesh, Vol. IV, p. 34)

DESPONDENCY — A DEVICE
OF THE EVIL INCLINATION

...You write to me that you find yourself in a state of despondency:

It is patently obvious that your despondent state is a device of, and results from, the machinations of the evil inclination, which seeks to obstruct man from fulfilling his purpose and task in this world — this task being, in the words of the *Mishnah*:[24] "I was created to serve my Master," a task that can only be accomplished with joy.

This is in keeping with the explanation of the "Great Teacher," the *Rambam*, (conclusion of *Hilchos Lulav*) who expresses this thought in wondrous and astonishing terminology — see his words there and take them to heart.

Having done so, you will then rejoice and exult in true joy, in keeping with the verse: "Know Him in all your ways." This degree of joy and the means of obtaining it is explained in *Tanya*, chapter 31 and onward — see there.

This [joyful manner of] service also leads to an increase in one's physical health, as we verily observe....

(Igros Kodesh, Vol. XIII, p. 104)

BECOMING AWARE OF FAULTS SHOULD
LEAD TO JOY, NOT DESPONDENCY

In reply to your letter ... in which you write about your general [dejected] state of mind, particularly of late, and you

---

24   *Kiddushin* 4:14.

conclude by stating that you are under the impression that you are currently undergoing some form of spiritual decline:

It is important for you to know that such imaginations in general, and particularly when they lead to despondency — as you write in your letter — come from the evil inclination and from the "other side" [of holiness], as explained in *Tanya* regarding the condition of melancholy (*atzvus*) and the utter necessity of banishing it.

This is particularly so, since you merited that G-d saw fit to place you in a resplendent environment, that being "a commandment [which] is a lamp, and the Torah, [which] is light" — [moreover, in the shining environment] of the "luminary of Torah," which is the "inner portion of Torah," [i.e., *Chassidus*]. Surely, then, you should be suffused with great joy at having merited this good fortune.

As to your feelings that you are deficient and flawed in a number of areas:

First of all, as stated above, it is possible that this is merely your imagination. Secondly, even if your opinion is based on fact, [then consider the following]:

It is similar to a person who was unwell and was oblivious to his ill health. Consequently, he did not safeguard himself from things that would be harmful to him and did not engage in things that would heal him, since he was under the impression that he was entirely healthy.

G-d then made it known to that person that he was unwell. It follows that this [newfound knowledge of his true condition] offers hope that the person will begin occupying himself in matters that will heal him, and [that from now on he will] distance himself from matters that are harmful.

Surely, the fact that the true state of affairs was revealed to this individual, [with the consequent benefit of the person being able to restore himself to good health,] should not lead him to a state of despondency. On the contrary, this knowledge informs the individual and serves as a preparation for his restoration to good health.

Undoubtedly, similar to the overwhelming majority of people, you also possess both elements: To some degree your thoughts about your deficiencies are based on fact, and to some degree they are exaggerated by the "other side."

To state it more accurately, [the evil inclination] presents the fault in [an improper context]; not in the correct area, but in another area.

(The [evil inclination's] intent in doing so is twofold:

When the person will make an effort to improve in an area that does not need improvement, it will actually have a negative effect on that area that is not in need of improvement. Moreover, [making an effort in the wrong area] will damage his efforts in improving himself in the area that truly is in need of improvement. This matter is explained at length in many places in *Chassidus* as well as in books of *Mussar*.)

In a more general sense: It is known [regarding] the verse, "Serve G-d with joy," that when one serves with joy then his service is performed with greater alacrity and is blessed with greater success. And although the person is aware of his [spiritually deficient] state, the [flawed] state of his animal soul should not inhibit the joy of his Divine soul, as explained in *Tanya*....[25]

(Igros Kodesh, Vol. VI, p. 246)

---

25   Ch. 31.

BANISHING SADNESS THROUGH CONTEMPLATING LOVE OF A FELLOW JEW

I am in receipt of your letter...:

Meditating on the theme of *ahavas Yisrael* will help banish your despondency.

You have surely studied in depth chapter 32 of the sacred work of *Tanya* as well as *Mitzvas Ahavas Yisrael* in *Sefer HaMitzvos*, [i.e., *Derech Mitzvosecha*,] of the Tzemach Tzedek.

(Igros Kodesh, Vol. X, p. 42)

COMBATING MELANCHOLY AND HOPELESSNESS THROUGH TORAH, PRAYER AND LOVINGKINDNESS

In reply to your letter of *Motzaei Shabbos Kodesh*, [*Parshas*] *Bereishis*, in which you write that you feel a sense of melancholy (*atzvus*) and hopelessness...:

It is well known that many, many chassidic discourses instruct us to recoil from a state and sense of *atzvus*, [and also discuss] how such a [negative] state of mind tremendously hinders one's efforts in combating the evil inclination. Accordingly, one must rid himself of this feeling at the earliest possible opportunity, as it does not stem from [the side of] goodness [and holiness, but from the opposite side].

[The manner of combating *atzvus* is] similar to combating all other negative manifestations: by increasing one's efforts in the direction of goodness [and holiness]. Even a small amount of light banishes much darkness, and how much more so when there is a great amount of light.

When you will study our sacred Torah assiduously and diligently, establishing fixed times for Torah study, permanently imbuing Torah within your soul, then your feelings of hopelessness and even melancholy will cease. For our holy Torah gladdens the heart and soul, as the verse states,[26] "G-d's commands are upstanding, gladdening the heart."

This is particularly so when you ponder the concept of individual Divine providence — that G-d, the Essence of Goodness, watches over each and every individual throughout that person's daily life, and moreover, watches over every aspect and detail of his life.

On his part, man need only see to it that he stand firmly attached to G-d and ensure that he is an open vessel [for G-d's Divine blessings]. Man does so by following that which was written above, which in general terms consists of strengthening oneself in the three areas of Torah study, prayer, and performing acts of lovingkindness.

May G-d grant you success in all the above, so that you will be able to convey to me the glad tidings that you are serving G-d with joy.

(Igros Kodesh, Vol. X, p. 33)

OVERCOMING A SENSE OF SPIRITUAL ANGST, HOPELESSNESS AND DESPAIR

I received your two letters — the first one undated and the second from *Adar* 22 — in a timely manner; however, the

---

26   *Tehillim* 19:9.

pressure of [my] activities did not enable me to respond until now....

I was very satisfied to read that you are making use of your artistic talent and are preparing an art exhibition, and that the media has given you good reviews....

Regarding the main part of your letter, where you bemoan your situation, feel brokenhearted, from time to time fall into despair, can find no place for yourself and so on, and you would like to meet with me in order to discuss the matter in person:

The meeting of two good friends always has positive value and brings spiritual satisfaction to both parties, but to delay tackling your problem until we are able to meet, and for you to continue meanwhile in the same mood of despair (G-d forbid) — this cannot be. Whom among us can afford such a thing?

You do not write exactly what leads you to such a frame of mind, which is why it is impossible for me to go into the details of it and demonstrate to you that these details are imagined and that your despondent disposition is merely a result of the enticements of the evil inclination.

By this I mean: Even if this matter, [i.e., the cause of your angst,] does have some basis in reality, the fact that it is being utilized to stir up within you a sense of hopelessness and despair is surely a machination of the evil inclination and lacks basis in reality. My father-in-law, the Rebbe, would label the evil inclination "the cunning one," since it uses the precise phraseology, [i.e., "it presses the precise button,"] that ensnares that particular person into its net.

I must interject here a general observation regarding this matter — doing so based on the maxim of the Baal Shem Tov

— oft repeated by my father-in-law, the Rebbe — that every Jew can learn a lesson in his spiritual service through all that he sees and hears.

[In light of the above,] I wish to illuminate your situation in particular:

You surely are aware that the primary skill and gift of an artist and painter lies in his ability to detach himself from the superficial appearance of the image with which he is working. He must be able to penetrate the true essence of the object and transform his impression into a picture with physical dimensions.

This artistic representation reveals to the viewer that which he could not recognize on his own, an essence that was obscured by superficial layers. Only an artist has the skill to reveal the inner dimensions of an object, thus enabling the observer to see it with a different perspective and realize the limitations of his previous awareness.

[So, too, in the analogue,] "In a manner corresponding in every detail to the said figure and image,"[27] does this apply in man's service of his Creator:

We know from Torah in general and from *Chassidus* in particular that all of Creation derives from G-d's Divine Utterances, which constantly create and animate everything. It is merely that G-d's power of concealment and contraction obscures these Divine Utterances and we see only the external [manifestation; i.e., we only see the end result, the actual creation, and not the Utterances that are the true and inner aspect of all that exists].

Man's spiritual service — based on the simple belief that there is "nothing aside from Him" — consists of applying this

---

27   Cf. *II Shmuel* 7:17, and *Tanya*, ch. 46.

principle in all areas of our life. Consequently, each of us, according to our abilities, is to reveal to the greatest extent possible the G-dliness within everything, and minimize as much as possible the concealing and obscuring aspect of the external manifestation [of creation] upon the inner dimension of G-dliness within it.

The same is true in particular regarding every Jew, all of whom are "Children to the L-rd your G-d."[28] Concerning this it is stated in *Tanya* (ch. 2) that "Just as a child is derived from his father's brain, so too is the soul of every Jew derived from G-d's thought and wisdom" and "He and His wisdom are one."

This, then, is the true essence and being of each and every Jew, including you as well.

Since G-d desired that the soul not have to receive its nurture from "bread of shame" (i.e., spiritual sustenance given gratuitously, without having been earned by the recipient), He therefore made it possible for man to serve Him; moreover, to serve Him in a manner that involves toil of body and soul. Through these endeavors one *earns* all manner of good, including the highest levels of spirituality.

The Alter Rebbe forewarns yet another matter in *Tanya* (conclusion of ch. 39):

We should not think that there are those who will not accomplish their soul's mission, which, the Alter Rebbe states, simply cannot be, for "even when one engages in Torah and *mitzvos* not for its own sake (*shelo lishmah*), he will certainly arrive at [study and observance] *lishmah*, ... because "no one banished from Him [by his sins] will remain banished."[29]

We must therefore be vigilant in preventing external

---

28   *Devarim* 14:1.

29   Cf. *II Shmuel* 14:14.

matters from obscuring man's essence and the intent and purpose of his being.

The various difficulties, tests and personal challenges of refining oneself and one's surroundings (*birurim*) are all means to the ultimate end — that the soul be able to arrive at its former state of purity prior to its descent into creation, as well as attaining even higher levels.

[The soul can accomplish this specifically here, in this physical world,] for "Better one hour of repentance and good deeds in this world than all the life in the World to Come."[30]

Consequently, one should not permit the difficulty of withstanding the tests [that are placed before the individual —] or even if from time to time one has not withstood these tests — from overpowering the joy that one is to feel at being "My son, My firstborn son, Yisrael,"[31] and from the assurance that we have from G-d Himself that "your people are all righteous."[32]

Therefore, when a Jew appears — particularly one who heard of the light of *Chassidus*, and more particularly, one who has himself studied *Chassidus*, and even more particularly, one who has been refined as a result of personal suffering — and writes that he is, G-d forbid, in a state of hopelessness and despair, and finds no place for himself, etc., then this is not only contrary to the Jewish belief system, but it is also contrary to rational thinking as well!

G-d offers His absolute and unqualified assurance that "no one banished from Him will remain banished," nor does He demand that man perform beyond his capacity (for "G-d does

---

30   *Avos* 4:17.

31   *Shmos* 4:22.

32   *Yeshayahu* 60:21.

not make unreasonable demands of His creatures"[33]), rather that he performs according to his abilities.

G-d then tells the person [that not only does he not have to perform to his capacity, but simply] that it will suffice if he, "Open up for Me [but the space] of the head of a pin, and I shall open up for you [a space as broad as] the opening of the *Ulam* [in the Holy Temple]."[34]

All the above is what G-d says [and assures]. A human being then comes along and says that matters are actually quite different — and thus the resultant feelings of hopelessness, throwing up your hands in despair, and deluding yourself into thinking that your spiritual state is in a relentless state of decline!

The question then is: "When the words of the disciples contradict the words of the master, to whom do we listen?"[35] [i.e., when G-d says one thing and you say another, who do you think is correct?]

This is the question you must pose to yourself: You imagine things one way and G-d says that it is not so — is there any question as to who is correct?

...When you begin doing that which you should be doing, even though you imagine that all you can begin to do is but [the size of] "the head of a pin," then G-d will grant you success and "open up for you [a space as broad as] the opening of the *Ulam*."...

(Igros Kodesh, Vol. IV, p. 222)

---

33   *Avodah Zarah* 3a.

34   See *Shir HaShirim Rabbah* 5:3; *Tanchuma* (Buber), *Toldos* 18.

35   *Kiddushin* 42b.

PUT THE SOMBER SIDE OF YOUR NATURE TO GOOD USE

...I must once again reiterate that which I have already told you many times: your gloominess and despondency (*marah shechorah*) are without foundation, and you are simply wasting your time and ruining your peace of mind, and — literally — your nerves, by fretting over concerns that have no basis in reality.

May G-d will it that very shortly you begin to put this somber side of your personality to good use, by increasing your diligence in Torah study — and not only the revealed portion of Torah but in *Toras HaChassidus* as well.

"And one [force, i.e., the force for good,] will strengthen itself against the other [force for evil]":[36] by binding yourself to diligent Torah study, your *marah shechorah* will decrease in your life. May G-d send you a speedy recovery, including [a speedy recovery from] your *marah shechorah* as well....

(Igros Kodesh, Vol. IV, p. 65)

BANISH YOUR NEGATIVE THOUGHTS

You write about your gloominess, despondency and sadness:

It is superfluous to expound at length about [the undesirability of] something that has already been ruled against by our holy *Nesi'im*, and as has been explained in *Tanya* and many other places, how we must completely

---

36   *Bereishis* 25:28.

distance ourselves from *atzvus* and *marah shechorah*.

One does so by ceasing to think such [black] thoughts. If one cannot achieve this; [i.e., he finds it impossible to simply stop thinking negative thoughts], then one can accomplish this by not thinking about oneself but about G-d — how He is the Essence of Goodness, etc.

When one truly desires [to banish these thoughts and feelings] and makes a concerted effort to do so, he will be successful [in his quest]. This is in accordance with the ruling of our Sages, of blessed memory: "If you strive, you will succeed."[37]

(Igros Kodesh, Vol. VIII, p. 341)

OVERCOMING A SENSE OF HOPELESSNESS

...Regarding the statement (from the author of the letter) about his feeling of hopelessness:

I am astonished that he is unaware that the endeavor to place feelings of hopelessness and the like in a person's mind is among the most *formidable* tactics used by the evil inclination in order to get the person from performing his duties [and fulfilling his purpose in life]:

For then, [i.e., since the person believes that he has no chance of ever succeeding, etc.,] what can be demanded of him and why make an effort [to succeed at all? This is particularly so] since he has already declared (to others as well as to himself) that he has given up all hope, etc.

---

37   See *Megillah* 6b.

Veritable proof that the source of the above [sense of hopelessness] emanates from the evil inclination [and is not a result of true clinical depression] is that his feelings of hopelessness have not minimized in the slightest his desires for physical pleasures.

(From a letter of the Rebbe, printed in Likkutei Sichos, Vol. XXXIX, p. 297)

SENSE OF HOPELESSNESS SHOULD BE ENTIRELY BANISHED

You write about [your difficulties regarding] your health and getting established, and you conclude that at times you reach a state of despair and hopelessness (*yi'ush*), and so on:

I surely need not expound at length that an attitude of hopelessness is totally inappropriate and undesirable, for our Torah — the Torah of Life — specifically commands us to "never give up hope."[38] Both *Tanya* as well as other books of *Chassidus* explain at length how there is absolutely no place for loss of hope.

In truth, the negation of hopelessness is an essential part of the faith of every single Jew — as all Jews are "believers, sons of believers" — that G-d is the Essence of Goodness and that it is He Who actually conducts this world and watches over each and every individual with individual Divine providence.

This, of course, leads to the inescapable conclusion that "Everything that G-d does, He does for the good"[39] — for

---

38   *Berachos* 10a.

39   *Ibid.,* 60b.

the particular goodness of the individual over whom He watches....

(Igros Kodesh, Vol. XVI, p. 295)

LOSS OF HOPE OF BEARING CHILDREN

This is a reply to your letter in which you write of your mood, your hope, and your request of G-d that you should bear healthy children.

Since this is one of the most important *mitzvos* in our holy Torah, "the Torah of Life,"[40] one must be firm in one's trust in the Creator of the world that He will make it possible for you and your husband to fulfill it.

However, it is self-understood that one cannot point to the calendar and tell G-d that this must happen when it feels right to oneself. For since G-d is the wellspring of good, He certainly knows what time is good, and that is when He will fulfill your hearts' desires in a positive way. One can only — with strong trust in the fulfillment of one's request — pray that this should come about as soon as possible.

As to what you write about losing hope, G-d forbid: a daughter of Israel must not say this, because G-d is omnipotent, and He desires that things should be good for every Jew not only on a spiritual level, but also on the actual material level.

With blessings that your prayers regarding the above subject will be fulfilled soon and that we should hear glad tidings from you,

(Igros Kodesh, Vol. XII, p. 109)

---

40   In the original, *Toras Chayim* (from the last blessing of *Shemoneh Esreh*).

BANISHING SUICIDAL THOUGHTS

...Contemplate, study repeatedly, and thoroughly memorize those themes that are elucidated in many places regarding the subject of individual Divine providence.

Realize that they are true in the simplest and plainest sense — that the Creator and Conductor of the world watches over every aspect of each and every individual in the minutest detail.

This will lead you to the inescapable conclusion that those matters about which you write should not constitute a source of worry and concern; surely there is no room for your request — or as you state in your letter, "a very strong request" — for the opposite of life, G-d forbid.

Meditate on the fact that the souls of each and every Jew emanate from under G-d's Throne of Glory and descend below into a physical body (and this is a tremendous descent, for there is absolutely no comparison between the soul as it exists above and the soul as it exists in the body below). Yet, this descent is worthwhile in order for the Jew to exist and be productive specifically in this world, which is to say that it is [specifically here that the Jew is] able to study Torah and perform *mitzvos*.

This leads to the understanding that each and every deed (for example, wearing *tefillin*) is so great that it is entirely beyond our comprehension. The same is true as well regarding all other matters of Torah and *mitzvos* (for the entire Torah is compared to *tefillin*).

Contemplating these matters and the like will enlighten your true condition in life — that you were granted the best of all opportunities: the ability to fulfill the Divine mission that G-d entrusted to you within this world, by leading your life in consonance with the directives of our Torah, the Torah of Life.

Work on these matters joyfully — as explained in the *Rambam* at the conclusion of *Hilchos Lulav,* and see also *Rambam's* ruling in the beginning of the second chapter of *Hilchos Deos.*

(Igros Kodesh, Vol. XIV, p. 201)

NEGATING THOUGHTS OF SUICIDE

...You write that you feel compelled to... [G-d forbid, put an end to your life].

Understandably, this is not true at all. No Jew is forced to do something that is, G-d forbid, opposite G-d's desire. I want you to take note as well that any effort in this direction will in any event prove fruitless, since as long as the soul does not fulfill the mission it was commanded from the Giver of the Torah, it is destined to be reincarnated again and again in this world [until it finally accomplishes its mission]. Merely, that when a person [not only does not fulfill the mission, but moreover is] the cause of its ruination, then his soul's future incarnation becomes even more difficult. I need not go on at length about something that causes so much anguish. Moreover, it is clear that all the reasons and excuses that you write about are claims that emanate from an unholy source and have absolutely no foundation in reality.

May G-d will it that you come to realize the truth, which is good, spiritually as well as materially. With blessings for glad tiding.

(Igros Kodesh, Vol. XIV, p. 205)

AWARENESS OF ONE'S PURPOSE IN LIFE ASSURES LIFE'S CONTINUATION

Your[41] letter of August 22 reached me with some delay. In it you present a fairly clear picture of yourself, your background, education, spiritual vicissitudes, and present state of mind which you describe in rather dismal colors, and you conclude with the hope that I may be of some help to you.

Permit me then to make an observation, which is strikingly evident from the general tenor of your letter, and which I believe also holds the clue to the solution.

Your whole letter — two and half closely typewritten pages — is full of your own expectations and disappointments, as if everybody owes you everything, but no one has a claim on you.

Yet even a brief reflection will clearly reveal that the universe we live in is ordered in a system of give and take, and the personal universe of the individual (the microcosm) must likewise conform to this system of reciprocal relationship. Consequently, when one disrupts or distorts this system, it must necessarily bring about a distortion in one's immediate surroundings, and especially in one's inner life.

Now, judging by your own description, Divine Providence and the society in general have been quite generous to you. You have been gifted with more than the average measure of intelligence and mental capacities; you have been given opportunities of education, etc. In other words, you have been on the receiving end, but — forgive me for being so blunt — it did not occur to you, judging from your letter, that you might owe something to the society; that you might have obligations

---

41   This is the first in a series of letters that the Rebbe wrote that saved this individual from committing suicide.

to participate in it actively and help to better it by putting to good use some or all of the mental gifts and capacities with which you have been endowed. Heaven knows that our society is far from perfect and that there is much to be done in the way of raising its standards of justice and morality. It is the basic duty of everyone to contribute one's share towards this end.

So far, I have been speaking in general terms. When the individual in question happens to have the good fortune of being a Jew, his duties and obligations go infinitely higher, especially in this day and age, after one third of our people (quantitatively, and much more so qualitatively) have been annihilated. For, everyone who has been spared that fate must now contribute not only his normal share, but also make up the terrible gap that has been created in the life of our tortured people. One must now work for at least two, towards the preservation of our people and fulfilment of its destiny.

As for the question, wherein lies the preservation of our people, and what is its historic destiny? — the answer is not difficult to find if we examine the pages of our history throughout the many centuries of our sojourn among the nations of the world. It is neither power, nor country, nor even a common language that preserved us in the past, but our Jewish way of life in accordance with the Torah, *Toras Chayim* (the Law of Life) and *Mitzvos*, whereby Jews live. Those who sought new ways, or staked the future of our people on other factors — and there were such groups who made such attempts, viz. Kuthites, Saducees, Hellenists, Karaites, etc. — disappeared without trace. Only the eternal Torah and *Mitzvos*, the true Jewish way of life, preserved us in the past, as will preserve us in the future. This is the golden thread that runs throughout our long history.

If the person turning to me with such a problem as you describe were a gentile, I would say to him: You are too much wrapped up with yourself, with your own emotions and feelings and aspirations. Stop being concerned with your own problems. The way to cope with such an emotionally charged situation is to stop trying to cope with it. You must get away from yourself, and begin to think of others. It is time to begin an active participation in the society; to give, and give generously. The opportunities are many, and the need is great. You have your choices: social work, charitable, or even scientific.

But you are a Jew, and your obligations go beyond the above. You must live like a Jew in your daily life, the Jewish way of life, the way of the Torah and *Mitzvos*, and you must use your influence with others in the same direction. Some people think the Torah and the Jewish way is "old fashioned," they are both misguided and unscientific. Truth never gets "too old," can never get stale. Only falsehood, half truth and compromise can not last long; but truth is enduring and timeless.

It may require courage and resolution to change one's way of life. But these are qualities with which youth is generously endowed, and you are a young man, nineteen, as you write. You are capable of facing this challenge boldly.

We are now in the very auspicious days of *Elul*, when the old year is about to give way to the new. This is the time of Teshuvah. "Teshuvah" is usually translated as "repentance," the turning over of a new leaf. It is this and more, for the real meaning of Teshuvah is "return" — return to the source, the source of truth, purity and holiness, the very essence of the Jew, whose soul is truly a part of the Divine above.

Wishing you a *Kesivah vachasimah tovah,*

(From a letter of the Rebbe in the year 5721)

IF UNABLE TO FREE YOURSELF FROM MARAH SHECHORAH, UTILIZE THIS TRAIT FOR TORAH STUDY

I received your letter from this past Wednesday, and as has become your "sacred" custom, you conclude with a request for a blessing for success [as you feel that things are not going well for you].

It would seem that as soon as you crossed the border into Canada, your thoughts became filled with despondency and dejection (*marah shechorah*) once again.

I have already told you a number of times that you and your wife *sheyichyu* must put an end to your *marah shechorah*. If there is no other alternative — [then consider that] it is explained in *Torah Or*[42] that *marah shechorah* can be utilized for diligence in Torah study.

[Using your *marah shechorah* extensively for diligence in Torah study will also have] the added benefit of protecting your health, as then you will not be morose over corporeal matters. [It will also have the positive effect of] providing you with spiritual sustenance, as you will be utilizing this trait for Torah study.

I await good news about your wife's health and also that you will begin doing the above. It matters not if you will only be doing so under duress and in an unenthused manner,[43] and also, that you both undertake to serve G-d with a feeling of joy.

(Igros Kodesh, Vol. V, p. 14)

---

42   *Toldos*, p. 19c.

43   In the original *v'lu yehei b'kabbalos ol.*

OVERCOMING ANGUISH
AND DISTRESS THROUGH BITACHON

After a pause [in your letter writing,] I was satisfied to receive your letter of the 8th of *Kislev* in which you write that your health has improved.

I concur with the professor [who stated] that your health problem stems from anguish and distress (*agmas nefesh*) — to be more precise, it derives from a certain degree of weakness in your *bitachon* (trust) in G-d, Who not only creates the world but also conducts it, doing so in a manner in which His providence extends to each and every detail of a Jew's life.

When you will think deeply about this matter, you will be convinced that "G-d is with me; I shall not fear. What can man do unto me!"[44] — so much so that, upon finding himself in a precarious situation, King David said, "I will fear no evil, for You are with me."[45] Because of this [great degree of *bitachon*,] David was able to overcome all manner of adversity.

This tale [about David's manner of conduct] was placed in the Torah — the word Torah also meaning "directive" — in order that this serve as a lesson to all Jews wherever they may be. [The lesson is as follows:] if the person will strongly persist in his recognition that "You are with me," this will lead to the concluding verse of the chapter, "Only goodness and kindness shall follow me all the days of my life...."

(Igros Kodesh, Vol. X, p. 133)

---

44   *Tehillim* 118:6.

45   *Ibid.* 23:3.

REALIZE HOW DESPONDENCY AFFECTS THOSE NEAREST AND DEAREST TO YOU

After not having heard from you for a long time, I finally received your letter dated *Shevat* 23, in which you describe your present [despondent] mood and also describe some of the past events in your life, [a number of which were unfavorable].

Notwithstanding the above, one must be "joyous and glad of heart,"[46] as explained in our holy Torah and elucidated at even greater length in books of *Mussar* and *Chassidus*, where logical reasons are offered for this [feeling of joy to be possible even in the face of severe difficulties].

In *Yad HaChazakah*, at the conclusion of *Hilchos Lulav*, the *Rambam* also expounds on how one is to perform a *mitzvah*: [it should be performed with great joy]. Moreover, the verse states, "Know G-d in all your ways"[47] — that [all forms of] service must be with "gladness of heart." This [service with joy] is also cited in *Tur* and *Shulchan Aruch, Orach Chayim* chapter 231.

If this manner of conduct is necessary for everyone, how much more so is it necessary for an individual who realizes that thinking about past conduct leads to a deterioration in health, or to a glum frame of mind. I trust that I need not expound [on this subject] at too great a length to someone like you.

May G-d help that from now on you will be strong in your *bitachon* in G-d, Who oversees every human being with individual Divine providence and Who is the Essence of

---

46   After *Devarim* 28:47.

47   *Mishlei* 3:6.

Goodness. It is He Who commanded us that a Jew should be calm and not perturbed, and should serve Him serenely and joyously.

This manner of conduct is particularly important when G-d grants an individual a wife and children, for the mood of the husband has an impact on the entire family as well.

(Igros Kodesh, Vol. XIX, p. 215)

OVERCOMING DESPONDENCY AND FEAR BY INGRAINING IN ONE'S PSYCHE THAT G-D PROTECTS US AND THERE IS NOTHING TO FEAR

...You write about your [dejected and fearful] state of mind:

You should reflect on how G-d, Creator and Conductor of the entire world, oversees each and every one of us and protects us from untoward things — all that is necessary is that your daily life be conducted in accordance with the directives of our "Torah of Life" and the performance of its commandments, concerning which it is stated,[48] "You shall live by them."

[You therefore have nothing to be upset or fearful about, for,] in the words of [King David,] the "sweet singer of Israel," "G-d is with me; I shall not fear."[49]

Contemplate the above again and again until it becomes ingrained in your psyche.

It would be proper for you to inspect the *mezuzos* of your home, assuring that they are all kosher according to Jewish

---

48   *Vayikra* 18:5.

49   *Tehillim* 118:6.

law. You should observe the fine custom of Jewish women to always give *tzedakah* prior to lighting candles *erev Shabbos* and *erev Yom Tov*.

(Igros Kodesh, Vol. XXIV, p. 117)

THERE IS NO ROOM FOR DESPONDENCY AS OUR SPIRITUAL BATTLES ARE NOW ACCOMPLISHED WITH JOY

I am in receipt of your letter of Wednesday and am amazed that you write there about your depressed state of mind, notwithstanding the fact that Divine providence placed you in the wonderful position of providing aid and encouragement to the downhearted and depressed.

[Our Sages declare]:[50] "The attributes of the Holy One, blessed be He, [reflect man's pattern] measure for measure," moreover, this is many more times so.] Surely G-d has encouraged — in many respects — that you never enter into such a [depressed] state, as the verse states,[51] "No illness shall befall you, for I am G-d your healer."

This is the manner of healing of the Creator and Conductor of the world: that there is no untoward situation from the very outset. This is not the case when healing follows an illness, where at least some vestige [of the illness] remains, as our Sages, of blessed memory, state in *Yoma* 86a.

May it be G-d's will that from now on you will place even

---

50   *Sanhedrin* 90a.

51   *Shmos* 15:26.

greater emphasis on the verse[52] "Serve G-d with joy," a manner of service that was so greatly stressed by our Rebbe, the Baal Shem Tov, by his disciples, and by their disciples.

This is particularly so in light of the ruling of the *Rambam* regarding the necessity of serving specifically in this [joyous] manner — see his wondrous words in *Hilchos Lulav*, which serve as a guide to those who are perplexed about this matter [— the necessity to serve G-d with joy].

This [manner of service is of particular importance] in our times when each and every individual requires additional strength to battle negative forces. For there is the known aphorism of my father-in-law, the Rebbe, that when a soldier goes out to battle, he does so singing a joyous song of victory, which in itself enables and hastens the victory, as is readily understood....

(Igros Kodesh, Vol. XIV, p. 420)

OVERCOMING DEJECTION THROUGH JOY

In reply to your letter ... written in the month of *Adar* II, a month in which one is to increase one's measure of joy throughout the month, particularly as your letter was written several days prior to Purim, when one's joy should be boundless:

Notwithstanding all the above, the content, and most importantly, the mood of your letter is not only not Purim-like, it is not even joyful.

After all the reasons and explanations that you provide in your letter [for your downheartedness], there still remains

---

52   *Tehillim* 100:2.

the command of G-d — He Who is not only the Creator of the world, but also its Conductor — that one is to serve Him with joy. Surely G-d is aware of all the reasons [that you mention in your letter which you attribute to your dejection,] and nevertheless He commands to be joyful.

This teaches us three things:

a) Since G-d demands this [joy from us], then surely He has provided us with the capacity and ability to realize it, as "G-d does not make unreasonable demands of His creatures," and "When He requests, He only requests according to their, [i.e., created beings,] capacity [to fulfill this request]."

b) Even in such a situation [where there seems to be nothing to be joyful about], there are ample reasons for joy; all that is needed is the desire to keep one's eyes open to those matters [from which one can be joyful].

c) In light of that which is explained in many texts, including the text of *Tanya*, ch. 26, [a despondent attitude is contrary to proper service of G-d]: When one wants to be victorious in battle, particularly a difficult battle, then one must go about this with joy, and an open [i.e., responsive] heart that is unblemished by any trace of worry and sadness in the world, as explained there in *Tanya* at length.

There is also known the saying of my father-in-law, the Rebbe, of blessed memory: "A soldier on his way to the battlefront sings a march of victory and joy," although he has yet to begin the battle. For the mindset of having firm faith and conviction in the certain victory in the approaching battle and the joy [that will result from this victory], in itself strengthens and hastens the victory in battle....

(Igros Kodesh, Vol. XIV, p. 481)

FINDING JOY AND BENEVOLENCE IN LIFE BY BEING BENEVOLENT TO OTHERS

I was truly astonished to read in your letter that you cannot find anything in your life to bring you joy — this, after having written that you have "thank G-d, two very delightful and religiously observant daughters."

Make an effort to minimize, as much as possible, thoughts such as, "What am I feeling?"; "Am I afraid of someone?" and so on.

Replace these thoughts with profound contemplation as to how you can assist and see to the needs of your neighbors or your relatives *sheyichyu.* Surely you will find many such matters [where you can be of benefit].

[Bear in mind that] one who acts benevolently toward one's friend is rewarded with G-d's benevolence to an even greater extent [than the benevolence shown toward the other].

Since all matters are to be accomplished through natural means as well, consult a doctor who is also a friend (*rofeh yedid*).

(From a handwritten response of the Rebbe, Tishrei 12, 5743)

THE GIFT THAT LIFTS ONE'S SPIRITS

Divine providence has granted you the opportunity to be of assistance to others — both to your family as well as others — through your communal activities (in the synagogue and the school, etc.). G-d has thereby granted you a great and blissful gift, something that should give you tremendous satisfaction.

You should thus continue in your present job. As to your

feeling that you should have a higher position there, [this should not be an impediment, for one's status] is not of primary importance in life — that which is of greatest import is the good that one can do, etc.

(From a handwritten response of the Rebbe)

"GLADNESS IS IN HIS PLACE"

...It would be worthwhile for you to study *Shaar HaBitachon* in the book titled *Chovos HaLevavos* and meditate on the matters that are explained there.

When you will contemplate — even for a short while — that each and every Jew believes with simple faith that there is "no place devoid of Him,"[53] and [contemplate as well] the known ruling of our Sages[54] on the verse "Strength and gladness are in His place,"[55] [then you will come to recognize the following]:

That in accordance with the verse "One may not enter the King's gate in a garment of sackcloth,"[56] [i.e., one may not serve G-d in a mournful state,] it is out of the question to disturb this joy of "Strength and gladness are in His place" through the depression of any individual, no matter who it is — even if the person temporarily thinks that there is justification for this assessment.

All the above does not require deep contemplation, for

---

53   *Tikkunei Zohar, Tikkun 57* (91b).

54   See *Chagigah* 5b: "There is no sadness before Him, as the verse states: 'Strength and gladness are in His place.'"

55   *I Divrei HaYamim* 16:27 — i.e., since one is always standing before G-d, one should always feel strong and joyful.

56   *Esther* 4:2.

even slight consideration [of it] will suffice [for you to realize
the truth and importance of these words]....

(Igros Kodesh, Vol. XI, p. 109)

OVERCOMING NEGATIVITY
AND DEPRESSION

I received your recent letter and the previous one. Needless
to say, I was somewhat taken aback by the tone of your letter.
It is a good illustration of how it is possible for a person to
read and to learn and to receive instruction from books and
teacher, and yet when it comes to actual experience all this
instruction goes by the wayside.

I refer to the things which you have surely learned in
[the books of] Mussar [Jewish ethical books] and especially
Chassidus about the fact of the *yetzer hara* [evil inclincation] to
instill spirit of depression, discouragement, and despondency
in order to prevent the Jewish person from fulfilling his
divine mission.

This is the most effective approach. If the *yetzer hara*
would attempt to dissuade the person directly from fulfilling
his mission, he would not be easily misled. However, instead,
the *yetzer* tries to discourage the person in all sorts of ways,
using "pious" arguments which, unfortunately often prove
effective at least in some degree.

This is exactly what has happened in your case, and I am
surprised that you do not realize it. The proof is that from
the information that I have received, I can see that you have
accomplished a great deal more than you imagine....

Considering further that every beginning is difficult, especially where there is a change of place, environment, language,
etc., and yet the beginning has proved so successful, one is surely justified in expecting that as time goes on, and the initial difficulties are minimized and overcome, there will be a more than
corresponding improvement in the good accomplishments....

Since one is only human, it is not unusual to relapse
occasionally into a mood of discouragement. But as has been
explained in the *Tanya* and in other sources, such a relapse
should only serve as a challenge to bring fourth additional
inner reserves and energy to overcome the tactics of the
yetzer hara and to do even better than before.

I trust that since you wrote your letter your mood and
outlook have considerably improved and that this letter
will find you in a completely different frame of mind.
Nevertheless, I am sending you this letter, since one is only
human and subject to changes of mood as mentioned above.

Finally, I want to say that the above should not be
understood to mean that if you do find yourself in the above
frame of mind you should try to conceal it and not write about
it. For our Sages have said, "when a person has an anxiety
he *should* relate it to others"[57] for getting something off one's
chest is in itself already a relief.

One should also bear in mind, as the Old Rebbe [Rabbi
Schneur Zalman] has stated most emphatically in the laws of
learning and of teaching children Torah, that a person who
is engaged in teaching children Torah should especially take
care of his health, as this has a direct effect on the success of
the work.

I trust therefore that you are looking after yourself in

---

57   *Sanhedrin* 100b.

matters of diet and rest, and that you will always be in a state of cheerfulness and gladness.

(From a letter of the Rebbe, dated 28 Teves, 5721)

TRANSFORMING ONE'S FEELINGS OF GLOOM AND DEPRESSION IN A STEP-BY-STEP MANNER

In reply to your letter in which you write about your present [dismal] state of mind and your [pessimistic] outlook toward the future, at least to the not-too-distant future, and you ask my opinion concerning this matter:

Understandably, I do not accept the foundations upon which you construct your [dismal and pessimistic] views and conclusions at all. By this I mean that I believe your [negative] state of mind to be only temporary and [your conclusions] not based on any [enduring] reality.

[Consequently,] the more you endeavor to cease [thinking these gloomy thoughts], the quicker your current mood and state of mind will change [for the better]. It is absolutely clear that you have the power and ability to be of benefit not only to yourself but to others as well.

Merely, like all matters in this world, it is almost always necessary to expend effort in order to reveal and develop this potential into reality. However, this is a degree of effort that is eminently attainable.

When a person will contemplate that his relatively brief efforts will benefit himself and also benefit others for many years — benefits for others that include either their spiritual or physical welfare or both, and that this benefit can then result in a series of unending benefits — then the person will easily understand that his efforts and exertions to achieve this end are well worthwhile.

Without a doubt, in the vast majority of instances, it is impossible to radically change one's frame of mind instantaneously. However, this is not what is required; it will suffice that upon receiving my letter you will resolve to begin moving in the proper *direction*, i.e., to begin leading an active and constructive life and begin taking the first step in this direction.

Having done so, proceed [to change] step by step, one step leading to the other. You will soon discover that in a not overly long period of time you will find yourself on the road to a life of self-contentment and satisfaction....

(Igros Kodesh, Vol. XIII, p. 147)

OVERCOMING FEELINGS OF DEPRESSION CAUSED BY LACK OF ADDITIONAL CHILDREN

I received regards from you through your husband, who also told me of your present [depressed] frame of mind. And while this is quite understandable, it is necessary to bear in mind that the ways of G-d are inscrutable, but always good, since He is the Essence of Goodness, and it is in the nature of the good to do good — however difficult it may sometimes be to comprehend.

Yet it is not at all surprising that a human being should not be able to understand the ways of G-d. On the contrary, it is quite easy to see why a human being should not be able to understand the ways of G-d, for how can a created being comprehend the Creator?

We must, therefore, be strong in our trust in G-d and let nothing discourage us or cause any depression, G-d forbid.

As a matter of fact, the stronger our *bitachon* in G-d and in His benevolence, the sooner will come the time when G-d's overtly revealed goodness is experienced. You should therefore be confident that G-d will eventually fulfill your and your husband's hearts' desires for good, to be blessed with additional healthy offspring.

(From a letter of the Rebbe, dated 22 Elul, 5730)

FORSAKING MOROSENESS

...First and foremost, you and other appropriate community elders are to convey my astonishment to ... regarding the fact that he has seemingly yet to forsake his path of serving G-d with an attitude of moroseness. That this path [of Divine service] is untenable needs no explanation, even to non-chassidim, as the verse [explicitly] states:[58] "Serve G-d with joy."

This is particularly so regarding individuals who belong to the community of chassidim, as there is a directive of the Baal Shem Tov concerning serving G-d with joy, most particularly so to those who verily observed G-d's miracles, that He took them out of their previous country, [viz., Russia]....

May G-d assist that individual in his ability to serve Him with joy, thereby enabling him to convey joyful reports.

(Igros Kodesh, Vol. VIII, p. 299)

---

58   *Tehillim* 100:2.

DISPELLING SADNESS AND MELANCHOLY THROUGH THE STUDY OF APPROPRIATE TEXTS

In reply to your letter of the 6th of *Elul* in which you write that you are sometimes sad and melancholy:

Since you begin your letter by stating that you learned in a *Yeshivas Erev* of *Chabad*, you are to ask the spiritual mentor there to learn those chapters in *Tanya* with you that speak about the disrepute of sadness and melancholy and how it can be overcome. Study this text a number of times until you have acquired a thorough knowledge of its contents. By doing so, you will feel better.

It would also be appropriate for you to check your *tefillin*. From now on, at least, begin observing the three well-known *shiurim* of *Chumash*, *Tehillim* and *Tanya*.

(Likkutei Sichos, Vol. XXXIX, p. 325)

FEELINGS OF REMORSE — DETERMINING THEIR SOURCE

...When a person is constantly filled with thoughts and feelings of remorse over past misconduct, it is important to determine the source of these thoughts, whether they are emanating from the good inclination [and as such should be acted upon], or from the evil inclination [and should be pushed aside].

The best way of determining this is by examining the consequences of these thoughts: If they lead to additional energy and vitality in the performance of *mitzvos*, conducting oneself to an even stronger degree according to Jewish law ... then this is proof that these thoughts emanate from a pure source.

If, on the other hand, they lead to sadness and melancholy and neglect and laziness, or to feelings of hopelessness, then this is an indication that this emanates from the evil inclination (which clothed and hid itself within the garments of "G-d fearingness"). For all the above hinder the individual in his service of G-d....

(Likkutei Sichos, Vol. XXXIX, p. 327)

DO NOT FASHION THOUGHTS OF GLOOM AND DOOM: REFRAIN FROM NEGATIVE THINKING — IT CREATES ACTUAL NEGATIVITY

In reply to your letter, which seems to indicate that I have not yet succeeded in lifting your spirits:

I believe that I have already told you many times that, according to that which is explained in *Sefarim* — not necessarily in books of *Chassidus* — one is not to manufacture thoughts of *marah shechorah* within this world. For by not creating such thoughts, it bodes well that these [negative] events will not come to pass at all.

Not only should we not create negativity through speech — similar to that which is stated in *Chassidus* (I believe this is printed at the conclusion of the *Siddur Meah Shearim*) that when the Mezritcher Maggid would think a new [Torah] thought, he would verbalize it in order to bring it down into this world — we should not even manufacture such negativity through thought.

The reason for this is as explained above; [i.e., that the negative event not become actualized as a result of his thinking it. What, in fact, should be done] is understood from the aphorism of our holy Rebbeim and *Nesi'im*, who were wont to say: "Think positively, and it will be positive."

You undoubtedly imagine that it is very difficult to influence your power of thought to think in this [positive] direction, [although this is not necessarily so. However,] if this proves to be the case, [i.e., that it is difficult for you], then endeavor to clothe your power of thought within thoughts of Torah; the spiritual good [and positivism of Torah] will filter down into physical goodness [and positivism] as well.

The thrust of all the above is that the more you strengthen your faith and trust in G-d — to the extent that it will impact even your thought, speech and action — the more you will succeed in implementing the above, and the greater will be your resulting material and spiritual sustenance.

(Igros Kodesh, Vol. VI, p. 286)

NEGATIVE THOUGHTS AND THEIR NEGATIVE EFFECT

I have just received your letter from *erev Shabbos Kodesh*. It seems from your letter that once again you are in a depressed mood, etc.:

Why impair your mental state by coming up with so many negative ideas and thoughts, Heaven forfend?

I have alerted you concerning this a few times in the past, yet it seems that this message has not *reached* you — or as that word[59] [in the Holy Tongue] is interpreted in *Likkutei Torah* at the beginning of *Parshas Shemini*, this message has not yet *touched* you....

(Igros Kodesh, Vol. VI, p. 276)

NEGATING NEGATIVE THOUGHTS AND QUESTIONS REGARDING ONE'S HEALTH

I acknowledge your letter of the 5th of *Teves* in which you write about your [poor] state of health and that this has shattered your spirit:

Abandon this path [of negative thinking]. G-d is, after all, the "Healer of all flesh and Performer of wonders."[60] Though it is impossible for us to discern G-d's intentions, which results in the evil inclination sometimes arousing within us unsettling questions and thoughts that hinder our spiritual and even physical health, we must always know that these questions and thoughts are merely a machination of the evil inclination.

We must be firm in our *bitachon* in G-d that in time He will grant us healing for our ailments. And until that time, we still remain part of G-d's world, acting as his emissaries fulfilling our mission of spreading light in our environs, illuminating our Divine and animal souls with the light of Torah and *mezutoraspirkei* , and our surroundings, by disseminating there the light of Torah and Judaism....

In order for all the above to be accomplished in the best possible manner, it is necessary that we do so with a feeling of joy,

---

59   The Hebrew word *higiya* carries both meanings.

60   After the text of the *Asher Yatzar* blessing.

as the verse states: "Serve G-d with joy."[61] When you strengthen yourself [by contemplating the above], surely you will be assisted from on High to succeed in actualizing this matter.

(Igros Kodesh, Vol. VIII, p. 111)

FINDING THE TRUE CAUSE FOR SADNESS AND DESPAIR AND RECTIFYING THE SITUATION WITH JOY

I received your letter in which you describe the state of your [physical] health, as well as your [sad and despairing] state of mind.

From what I can ascertain from your letter, I must emphasize that there are various aspects of your life for which you can be truly grateful to G-d.

Understandably, this does not mean that the tormented state in which you now find yourself is completely without basis. Nevertheless, a person must be able to see the complete picture [including all the good that has transpired in his life, and] not only the negative part.

It should not be difficult for a woman with a background like yours and possessing faith such as you do to contemplate G-d's benevolent providence, which He provides to each and every one individually. Moreover, G-d is the Essence of Goodness, and "It is in the nature of he who is good to do good."

When one ponders these thoughts, one must inevitably come to the same conclusion as did King David, the author of

---

61   *Tehillim* 100:2.

the Psalms, who declared: [62] "G-d is with me; I shall not fear."

To the contrary, you have all the reasons to be joyous and glad of heart, particularly since a joyous attitude on your part will have a beneficial effect on your entire family. Merely, it is important for you to bear in mind, as mentioned above, that you indeed possess many things for which you should be grateful and which should cause you joy.

It happens quite often that an individual whose mood is similar to yours seeks to discover the basis for his [unhappy] frame of mind, thinking that the answer he comes up with is the true cause for all his problems [and unhappiness], when in truth the root cause may be something else entirely.

This is particularly true of a Jewish man or woman whose true joy is entrenched in living a full Jewish life, i.e., a life that is in complete harmony with the path of Torah and *mitzvos* given to us on Sinai and that made us into a holy nation. The particulars of how to live a Jewish life are meticulously detailed in the *Shulchan Aruch*, a book that spells out Jewish law and daily conduct.

If for one reason or another one's daily life is not in complete accord with the Jewish way of life as commanded by G-d, it is impossible for a Jew to be completely happy and content, inasmuch as something vital is missing from his life. It is possible that the person is unaware of this, for which reason he will search for the cause of his discontent and unhappiness in other areas.

On the other hand, when a Jew is steadfast in his outlook that he will live in complete harmony with the Jewish way of life, then he is capable of being completely happy and content.

The above is something that can be achieved by every

---

62   *Ibid.* 118:6.

Jew, although for some it may be easier than for others. This capacity surely exists since G-d, the Creator and Conductor of the world and the Commander of these commandments, also provides the person with the capacity to fulfill His commands.

Of course I am aware of the question of how it is that there are many individuals who are seemingly detached from the path of Torah and *mitzvos* and nevertheless seem to be completely happy, and so on.

The answer is simple. No one really knows what is transpiring in the heart and mind of another individual. Additionally, a person can conceal his inner dissatisfaction and unhappiness, although sooner or later this must come to the fore.

It would be worthwhile for your husband to check his *tefillin*, and before he puts them on each weekday morning he should give a small coin to *tzedakah*. It would also be worthwhile that the *mezuzos* in your home be checked to assure that they are kosher according to Jewish law. You as well should give a small coin to *tzedakah* prior to lighting candles.

I hope to hear from you good news.

(From a letter of the Rebbe, dated 12 Kislev, 5725)

THE SPIRITUAL EFFECTS OF GROUNDLESS DESPAIR AND LOSS OF HOPE[63]

1) I received [your letter that contained the good news that

---

63   The above is a handwritten response of the Rebbe to an individual who had a lung tumor. Additional X-rays revealed that most of the tumor had mysteriously disappeared. The person writes to the Rebbe that notwithstanding the above, he still feels his situation is hopeless.

the tumor has largely vanished]. Thank you ever so much for the good news.

2) I was understandably stunned and shocked when I read this, [i.e., that you have given up hope, etc.]. You witnessed a clear miracle from Heaven — and then you write this?!

May G-d in His abundant mercy forgive you, and may no impression remain [Above] from your letter.

(from a handwritten response of the Rebbe)

NEGATIVE FANTASIES OF HOPELESSNESS AND DESPAIR

...You *write* that you suffer from an ailment — although you don't say what it is — and that at any moment you are likely to undergo a serious heart attack, etc., G-d forbid. (It appears to me that this is not the case, and that — begging your pardon — this is an extreme exaggeration.)

You write further that a partition of iron is separating [you from your Father in Heaven] and that your prayers and charitable contributions have had no effect, and so on.

Without a doubt, you yourself also understand that all this is no more than fantasies. For even if there were a partition of iron, the Sages assure us in plain words that "even a partition of iron cannot separate the Children of Israel from their Father in Heaven."[64]

The same applies to what you write about how your prayers and especially the *tzedakah* (charity) you distribute have had no effect. I saw in a little book — it's called the *Tanach* —

_____

64   *Pesachim* 85b.

where it is written (*Malachi* 3:10) that the Holy One, blessed be He, says: "Test Me, please, in this," in the *mitzvah* of *tzedakah* — that if only people will give *tzedakah,* "I will pour down blessings upon you," and so on. The same applies to prayer, as is explained in many sources in the teachings of the Sages.

Above all, as is clarified in the works of *Chassidus,* this is one of the counsels by which the evil inclination plunges a man into melancholy. And if one must be vigilant not to fall into melancholy over spiritual reasons, how much more wary must one be of melancholy that comes from some other source, for there is nothing worse than that.

You should consistently fortify your trust in what even the most feckless of Jews believe — that the Holy One, blessed be He, is not only the Creator of the world but that He also conducts it, and not only long ago, but also presently, every day and at every hour. Moreover, He conducts not only the world in macrocosm, but also all the affairs of the microcosm, man.

G-d, who is the ultimate good, will no doubt enable you to see, even with eyes of flesh, that everything will be for the best, even in the kind of good that is visible.

For this, however, one must strengthen one's bonds of *hiskashrus* with the G-d of Life — by setting aside fixed times to study the Torah of Life; by serving Him through the service of prayer — acting benevolently toward your Living Soul; and by fortifying your observance of the *mitzvos,* and of the comprehensive *mitzvah* of *tzedakah,* for "the truth of tzedakah is for life."[65]

I hope that in the near future you will let me know of an improvement in your material situation and likewise an improvement in your spiritual situation — namely, the disappear-

---

65   *Mishlei* 19:21.

ance of thoughts about a separating partition, etc., etc. — and that you will make strenuous endeavors to fulfill the command of the Holy One, blessed be He, to: "Serve G-d with joy."[66]...

(Igros Kodesh, Vol. IV, p. 292)

LIFE'S "DESCENTS" ARE NO CAUSE FOR DISPIRITEDNESS

...A person's life does not always proceed smoothly, and since one has the will and the capacity to ascend, this very fact also creates the possibility of descent.

Accordingly, one should not become overwrought or dispirited (G-d forbid) when one observes a descent, especially when that descent relates only to material things, and especially since it happened through no cause of your own.

Indeed, a descent ought to arouse — from deep within oneself — greater powers of faith and trust, whose external manifestation is a courageous spirit and a lack of emotional reaction to an unpleasant phenomenon, particularly when it lasts only very briefly....

(Igros Kodesh, Vol. VIII, p. 128)

---

66   *Tehillim* 100:2.

chapter 3

CONQUERING ANXIETIES, FEARS, WORRIES AND "NERVES"

ACHIEVING
A TRUE STATE OF HAPPINESS

I am in receipt of your letter of August 21, in which you write about the way of life that your son has recently chosen for himself, having become more religious and observant, devoting time to the study of the Torah, etc., all of which has seemingly filled you with anxiety, as your opening sentence expresses it: "Where are our children going?"

Since your profession is connected with the science of medicine, especially chiropractic, which even more than the other branches stresses the importance of the nervous system for the proper functioning of the entire organism, and no doubt also with the emphasis on the need of the nerves' functioning without outside pressure, it makes it easier for me to explain my position in regard to the question raised in your letter.

My position is based on the authority of our wise ancients, whose views pertinent to our subject matter have been gaining increased recognition even by modern medical science, namely, that physical health, not to mention spiritual, or, to use a modern idiom, "peace of mind," is conditioned upon inner security, and the absence of mental (I would say, spiritual) pressures, since any such pressure brings disorder in the normal and proper functioning of the nervous system, thereby affecting sooner or later the proper functioning of the organism. In other words, the most important factor in the happiness of a human being is not so much the externality of things per se, but that the person should feel free to conduct his life in accord with his inner spiritual faculties, convictions and desires.

Not many years ago, "peace of mind" was variously predicated on the attainment of certain goals: To the materialistically inclined it meant the amassing of wealth, which they felt would give them security; others sought security in scientific progress, considering modern science as the panacea of all human ills; still others sought security by identifying themselves with a certain movement or ideology, such as socialism, communism, fascism, etc. Finally, there are those who can find security only in religion and faith.

In recent years, however, especially in the last decades, it was clearly demonstrated that wealth offered no security, for we have seen how economically "secure" families have been impoverished overnight. Similarly disappointing have proved political regimes and social movements and "isms" of all sorts. As a result, an overwhelming feeling of insecurity has taken root among growing youths and thinking adolescents, reflected in their vacillation from one extreme to the other, in emotional and mental disturbances, in Juvenile delinquency and rebelliousness, *etc.*, which have spread alarmingly in recent years, as is even better known to the medical profession than to laity.

In the present disturbed society and environment, it is, therefore, more vital than ever before that the young generation should feel *terra firma* under their feet. This solid basis can be provided only by finding religion. Consequently, when one's own child has happily found this security, it should be regarded as G-d's greatest blessing. For far from being a disturbing factor to their happiness, it is The Factor, one and only, which will ensure their true happiness. It goes without saying that nothing should be done to jeopardize this factor, not even by any form of pressure, which could only bring disturbance and distortion and unavoidable consequences.

If it is detrimental to bring pressure to bear on any spiritual factor, how much more so in regard to faith. For the essence of our faith is to accept G-d and His precepts as an area which lies above and beyond human comprehension. For, on the one hand to profess faith in G-d and Divine Power and Authority, and on the other to place His commandments under the scrutiny of one's own human intelligence, picking and choosing only that which seems to him "rational", is a contradiction in terms, since no matter how intelligent a person is, his intelligence is finite and limited and cannot be used as a yardstick in the realm of the Infinite. It would therefore be just as illogical and unjustified to attempt any kind of pressure to influence somebody else against his religious beliefs and dictates.

I do not know your son personally, but I have had occasion to meet your daughter-in-law several times while she was a student at Beis Yaakov. Since she has chosen your son as her life's partner, I can safely assume that your son's natural faculties and inclinations tally with hers. I therefore congratulate you and Mrs.... on having been blessed with such a fine son and daughter-in-law. I am quite confident that if they follow the way of life which you describe, they will be increasingly happy, and you and your wife will have ever growing *Nachas* from them, for, in the final analysis, children's happiness is the parents' true *Nachas*...

Much more could, of course, be said on the subject matter of our correspondence, but I trust that I have made my position clear to you, and for a person of your standing it will be adequate. I am firmly convinced that the path chosen by your son which, as is evident from your letter, is in complete harmony with that of his wife, is the one that assures their true happiness, and I prayerfully hope that you and your wife will give them every encouragement in that direction..

(From a letter of the Rebbe, dated In the Days of Repentance 5719)

NEEDLESS WORRIES — A NEEDLESS WASTE OF ENERGY

Your letter duly arrived, but numerous preoccupations did not allow me to reply until now. As a matter of fact, you don't need my reply, because you received a reply from my revered father-in-law, the Rebbe [Rayatz], when you were here.

Nevertheless, I would like to reiterate something that I have already said a few times:

One ought to know, once and for all, that faith is not something that is meant to remain only in one's thoughts; it must permeate the whole of one's life.

You are, without any doubt, a believer. So, the very first point of belief is that G-d directs the world. And if He is capable of directing one-and-a-half billion people, then your own affairs will certainly see the fulfillment of the verse,[1] "I have made you and I will carry you; I will sustain you *and deliver you.*"

Now, think this over. G-d promises, "I will sustain and

---

1   *Yeshayahu* 46:4.

deliver you." So think: Can a gentile from this or that land disturb G-d from fulfilling His promise (G-d forbid)? Having thought that, now consider:

Is G-d really in need of your worry as to how He is going to run your affairs and solve your problems? Or will He succeed in finding good solutions even without your worrying?

After all is said and done, you must remember that the Rebbe — that is, my revered father-in-law, of saintly memory — gave you his blessing, and the blessing of a *tzaddik* is certainly fulfilled. So the blessing you received will also be fulfilled.

However, *until* you see the fulfillment of the blessing, you have been given two options:

Either (a) you will walk around worried in case (G-d forbid) the blessing won't be fulfilled. And then, when the blessing *is* fulfilled, you will have a fresh worry: Why did you have to waste so much vital energy in vain?

Or (b) you will be staunch in your trust and faith in G-d — that He will lead you along the right path and will fulfill all the blessings that you have been given. And then, when you see them being fulfilled in actual fact, you will be able to tell yourself: "Just look how well I handled this situation! I didn't worry about things that were no cause for concern."

This is one of the meanings of my father-in-law's blessings to you, and not only as a blessing but also as a directive. Be happy, because — with G-d's help — the problems that you imagine to be so serious will be solved.

You have nothing to worry about. You can be happy, and you can fulfill the directive of the verse,[2] "Serve G-d with joy."...

(Igros Kodesh, Vol. IV, p. 255)

---

2   *Tehillim* 100:2.

FEELINGS OF INSECURITY

...A Jew can attain internal and external harmony only by living life as he or she is supposed to live it. If, for whatever reason, one's daily conduct and life are not as they should be, this disturbs the person's harmony and creates a feeling of restlessness, insecurity, etc.

Sometimes this feeling rises unconsciously. And sometimes, as you mention in your letter, it comes as a result of having a troubled conscience, all the more so since there is a special Jewish conscience over and above the general human conscience that is common to all decent human beings, Jews and non-Jews alike.

(From a letter of the Rebbe)

FEELINGS OF DISQUIETUDE AND CONFLICT

...It has been explained in our Torah — and this has also been confirmed by modern science — that a surface layer may cover up an essential trait or quality, or, to use modern terminology, the subconscious may be overlaid by the conscious mind.

In such a case, conflicts are inevitable, for man's essence is linked to the deep internal layers and not the surface "cover," which itself is subject to change and under the influence of external forces.

For a Jew to eliminate conflict, it is necessary for him to

bring to the fore his inner essence,[3] which is his deep-rooted faith in G-d. Failing this, he is bound to feel perturbed, even though the cause may be concealed from him.

In other words, a Jew must live his daily life in accordance with the Torah and *mitzvos* — the Jewish way of life — for it is only in this way that he can attain true harmony and peace of mind.

Needless to say, it is not easy to transform one's daily life and routine, transforming it into a way of life that has not been practiced in the past.

However, inasmuch as this is the will and the directive of G-d, the Creator of man, it is clear that the Creator does not expect the impossible from His creatures, and that He has provided every Jew with the ability to live at the level that He has willed.

It does, however, require an effort, oftentimes a strenuous effort and much determination, including at times the sacrifice of certain conveniences, whatever they may be.

But considering what is at stake — nothing less than the attainment of peace of mind and inner harmony, and even plain physical health (inasmuch as the physical and the spiritual are interrelated) — every effort made in this direction is surely worthwhile and most rewarding.

I would suggest that as a start you begin putting on *tefillin* every weekday morning, and that in addition you say at least a short prayer. The *tefillin* should be checked first to ensure they are kosher....

(From a letter of the Rebbe in the year 5725)

---

3   *Rambam, Hilchos Gerushin,* conclusion of ch. 2.

FEELINGS OF INSECURITY

...In reference to your writing about doubts and the difficulty of making decisions, and about a general feeling of insecurity, it is unnecessary to elaborate to you at length that such feelings arise when a person thinks that he is alone and can only rely upon himself and his own judgment, and therefore feels doubtful and insecure about each move he has to make.

And while he also trusts in G-d, this trust is somehow superficial, without permeating him and his way of life in every detail; and [when it does, it does so] only on certain days, such as the High Holy Days, [when] he feels closer to G-d.

But when a person's faith in G-d is deep, and when he reflects that G-d's benevolent providence extends to each and every person, and to each and every detail, and each and every minute, surely he must develop a profound sense of security and confidence....

(From a letter of the Rebbe, dated 25 Elul, 5735)

ACUTE ANXIETY

This is to acknowledge receipt of your letter with the enclosure, in which you write about your problem of acute anxiety, and ask my advice.

The best and most effective thing to do, in a situation such as yours, is to study thoroughly those sections and chapters in our sacred books where the matter of Divine Providence and *Bitochon* are discussed, such as *Chovos Halvovos, Shaar Habitochon,* and similar.

It is well to keep in mind those chapters and verses in

the *Tehillim* which speak of these subjects, as well as the *Midrashim* and interpretations of our Sages on them.

These things should be studied with such depth that they should become a part of one's thinking. In this way there will be no room left for any kind of anxiety or worry, and as King David said in the *Tehillim*,[4] "G-d is with me, I shall not fear. What can man do unto me!"

As you well know, the matter of *Hashgocho Protis* is the basis of true monotheism, a concept which to us means not only that G-d is one, but that there is oneness in the whole of Nature.

In other words, the whole universe has one Supreme Being, Who not only is the Creator of everything, but also is the Master, continually supervising every detail of his handiwork.

The corollary of this is that there cannot be a single point in the whole order of the world which is separated from the Supreme Being, or in any way not subject to His control. At the same time it is obvious that the Supreme Being is also the Essence of Perfection and Goodness.

And although many things in the world seem imperfect, and require completion or perfection, there can be no doubt that there is a perfect order in the world, and even the lowest in the scale of Creation, namely the inanimate things, display wonderful perfection and symmetry, as can be seen from the atoms and molecules of inorganic matter.

Hence, the conclusion must be that even those things which require completion are also part of the perfect order, and necessary for the fulfillment of the good, as all this is explained at length in the teachings of *Chassidus*.

It is explained there that in order for a man to attain

---

4   *Tehillim* 118:6.

perfection, it is necessary that he should also have the feeling that he is not only on the receiving end, but also a contributor, and according to the expression of our Sages of blessed memory, "A partner in the Creation."[5] This is why many things have been left in the world for him to improve and perfect.

I also want to make the further observation, and this is also essential, that there is really no basis for anxiety at any time, and as you yourself mentioned in your letter, that you find no reason for it.

Even in such cases where you think you know the reason for your anxiety, the reason is undoubtedly imaginary, or at any rate, not the real cause. For the real cause is that one's daily life is not in complete harmony with the true essence of a Jew.

In such a case it is impossible not to have an awkward feeling that things do not seem to fit somehow, and it is this disharmony which is at the bottom of the anxiety, and it is in proportion to the discrepancy between his way of life and his true natural self.

Everybody recognizes that anxiety has to do with the psyche. But in the case of a Jew, the so-called psyche is really the *Neshama*. Some Jews have a particularly sensitive soul, in which case the above-mentioned disharmony would create a greater anxiety. In such a case even subtle and "minor" infractions of *Dikdukei Mitzvos* would create anxiety.

But even in the case of an ordinary soul of the average Jew, there must inevitably be created some anxiety if there is a failure to observe the fundamental *Mitzvos*. It is very possible that the above may have a bearing on your situation.

If this is so, then all that is necessary is to rectify matters,

---

5   *Shabbos* 10a.

and bring the daily life and conduct into complete harmony with the essence of the soul, through strict adherence to the *Torah* and *Mitzvos*. Then the symptoms will disappear of themselves.

It is necessary to mention also that in your case, where your position gives you a great deal of influence on your environment, your influence is an integral part of your harmonious life, and it is therefore essential that your influence, too, should be in harmony with the *Torah* and *Mitzvos* in the fullest measure.

I suggest that you should also have the *Mezuzos* of your home checked, as also your *Tefillin*, and before putting on your *Tefillin* every weekday morning, to put aside a small coin for *Tzedakah*.

(From a letter of the Rebbe, dated 26 Teves, 5725)

FEELING OVERWHELMED

Several decades ago, medicine discovered that the body could avoid certain illnesses through vaccination — i.e., inoculation with a radically weakened strain of those diseases one desires to guard against. Through this process, the body produces antibodies — custom-made weapons to guard against the illness.

The principles of healing the body, according to Maimonides, apply equally to remedies of the soul. This can provide us with a positive way of viewing minor difficulties in the execution of an important project. A weak dose of opposition early on in a venture can serve as a "vaccine" against more severe and difficult adversity later on.

(Igros Kodesh, Vol. XI, p. 58)

FEARS AND PANIC ATTACKS

BE INATTENTIVE, HEEDLESS AND UNMINDFUL

In reply to your letter with the enclosed *pidyon nefesh* — which I will read at a propitious time at the holy resting place of my father-in-law, the Rebbe — in which you write that you are fearful and panicky, etc.

Generally, matters such as these do not have a basis in reality (except for the fact that the person thinks and obsesses about these thoughts). Therefore, ceasing to think these thoughts (*hesach hadaas*) eliminates them entirely.

It is well known that *hesach hadaas* does not mean doing battle with a particular thought, for battling a thought is also contrary to ceasing to think about it.

Rather, it means, plainly and simply, to think about other matters entirely — when the troubling thought arises in his mind, he ignores it entirely; most definitely the person will not let the thought grow or battle it. Rather, he will push it aside by thinking about something else.

More specifically, these thoughts are banished by thinking about matters of Torah and *mitzvos* — for even a small measure of light banishes a large measure of darkness.

Understandably, all the above can be best achieved when a person is strong and healthy, which is why you should ask a doctor about your symptoms and follow his instructions. However — as stated above — do so without dwelling on the matter, i.e., whether you feel panicked, and so on and so forth.

[You can gain additional confidence that you will succeed in your quest of ridding yourself of your fears,] as we now find ourselves [in the midst of the period of the High Holidays,] in the days of being signed and sealed for the good. [At this time,] G-d, the Essence of Goodness, causes goodness to descend below upon each and every Jew, in an overtly revealed manner.

(Igros Kodesh, Vol. XVI, p. 13)

COMBATING FEARS AND ANXIETIES BY COMMITTING TO MEMORY THE FIRST SECTION OF CHAPTER 41 IN TANYA

...You write about your fears and anxieties:

It would be of benefit to you to examine your *tefillin*. Also, commit to memory the beginning of chapter 41 in the holy *Tanya* until the word *haMelech* found at the beginning of p. 56b. Review these words [often] in your thoughts, or even verbalize them.

(Igros Kodesh, Vol. XVII, p. 331)

COMBAT FEARS THROUGH ADDITIONAL MEASURE OF TZEDAKAH

...You write that at times your wife, [who is pregnant,] is sometimes overly anxious and fearful:

You should inspect the *mezuzos* in your home as well as your *tefillin*. Surely your wife conducts herself according to the good Jewish custom of fine Jewish women, the custom of giving *tze-*

dakah prior to lighting candles *erev Shabbos* and *erev Yom Tov*.

In addition to the above, your wife should give several cents to *tzedakah* every weekday morning until after she gives birth in a good and auspicious hour.

(Igros Kodesh, Vol. XIII, p. 180)

COMBAT FRIGHTENING IMAGES THROUGH CHASSIDIC TALES, BEDTIME SHEMA AND HAMAPIL

...You write that your grandmother's thoughts are filled with disturbing and frightening images:

It would be appropriate to check the *mezuzos* of her room. She should also give several cents to *tzedakah* every weekday morning.

Before retiring for the evening, she should read or have read to her — depending on her health — stories from our holy Rebbeim, as well as stories of chassidim in general. Your grandmother surely recites the bedtime *Shema* — at least the first section, as well as the blessing of *HaMapil*....

(Igros Kodesh, Vol. XV, p. 13)

COMMITTING WORDS OF TORAH TO MEMORY INCREASES G-D'S BLESSINGS AND PROTECTION

In reply to your letter in which you write that at times you are terrified of lightning and other similar matters:

Commit to memory several chapters of *Mishnayos* and at least one chapter of *Tanya*. From time to time, review them while you walk in the street and the like.

The fact that words of our Torah — given by G-d, Creator of the world — are embedded within your mind will increase G-d's blessings, protecting you in all your affairs.

(Igros Kodesh, Vol. XVIII, p. 124)

FEAR OF AN AYIN HARA

You write about an individual who is fearful that an *ayin hara* ["evil eye"] has been cast upon him:

In matters such as these, the fear can be totally nullified by not paying it, [i.e., the fear of the *ayin hara*,] even the slightest attention — not thinking about the matter at all.

(from a letter of the Rebbe)

FOLLOWING THE PATH OF TORAH NEGATES FEAR OF AN AYIN HARA

...You write about an "*ayin hara*":

It is explained in our Torah, called *Toras Chayim* and *Toras Emes*, because it is our guide in life and all its teachings are true, that when a Jew conducts his daily life in accordance with G-d's Will, as set forth in the *Shulchan Aruch*, he is thereby keeping the channels needed to receive G-d's blessings wide open. There is then no room for fear or anxiety.

For, as frequently stated in our Holy Scriptures, "G-d is

with me, I shall not fear;" "He sends His angels to guide you in all your ways;" and many other verses in this vein.

If you have not had your *mezuzos* checked recently, it would be well to have them checked to make sure they are kosher and properly affixed.

(From a letter of the Rebbe, dated 7 Iyar, 5737)

MENTAL HEALTH — NOT AN EVIL SPIRIT

...With regard to that which you write about Mr. ... from Bashar, who told you about what is transpiring with his son... [and fears that it may be the result of an evil spirit].

You should explain to him that this is merely a matter of [his son's mental] health and not — Heaven forfend — a matter of an evil spirit.

Physical wellbeing is primarily dependent on spiritual wellbeing; one must, however, utilize natural means [of healing] as well. [Mr. ...] should [therefore first] inspect the *mezuzos* in his home as well as his *tefillin*. I am referring not so much to the boxes that house the parchments of *tefillin*, but to the parchments [and writing] themselves, that they be kosher according to Jewish law.

The mother of the boy should scrupulously observe matters of *tznius*, most importantly with regard to the laws and regulations of family purity.

Prior to lighting candles *erev Shabbos* and *erev Yom Tov* as well as every Monday and Thursday during the week, his wife should give several francs to *tzedakah*.

Their son should wear a *tallis kattan* and be scrupulous

about keeping his head covered (*kisui harosh*).

In addition to all the above, they should seek the advice of a noted psychiatrist from a large city and follow his instructions....

(Igros Kodesh, Vol. XI, p. 303)

"A CASE OF NERVES"

...You write that you are under the impression that you are having heart palpitations:

It is almost certain that this is merely a product of your imagination — at most, it is merely a case of nerves. However, in order to set your mind at ease, you should visit a heart specialist and follow his instructions. All this pertains to your physical conduct.

With regard to your spiritual conduct:

Firmly fix in your thought, with the strength and intensity of faith that is possessed by all Jews, "believers, sons of believers," that G-d — Who created the world 5,711 years ago[6] and constantly recreates the world and conducts it according to His will — is the ultimate of goodness, and it is in the nature of He Who is good to do good.

This being so, it is obvious that your personal affairs are included in the above — that in your life and in your affairs *G-d* is the Master, and He will lead you to your ultimate [good] destination.... May it be G-d's will that He direct you with manifest and overtly revealed love, goodness and mercy.

Put all thoughts of "nerves," etc., out of your head. A chassid must be healthy not only spiritually, but physically as

---

6   This letter was written in the year 5711.

well, so that he may himself fulfill, and act as an instrument — meaning, through him his soul's mission is fulfilled, for which purpose his soul descended into the physical and corporeal world.

With blessings that in the immediate future you will convey to me glad tidings with regard to all the above.

(Igros Kodesh, Vol. IV, p. 262)

SPIRITUAL AIDS TO HELP CALM THE NERVES

...You write about your wife's health and that the doctor is also of the opinion that it is a case of nerves:

It would be worthwhile for you to inspect the *mezuzos* in your home to insure that they are all kosher according to Jewish Law. Additionally, your wife should give several cents to *tzedakah* every Monday and Thursday during the week.

This is in addition to the fact that surely your wife conducts herself according to the good Jewish custom of fine Jewish women, the custom of giving several cents to *tzedakah* prior to lighting candles *erev Shabbos* and *erev Yom Tov*.

She may rest assured that the "Healer of all flesh, and Performer of wonders" will grant both of you lengthy years filled with all manner of good.

(Igros Kodesh, Vol. XII, p. 91)

BE INATTENTIVE AND THE ATTACKS OF NERVES WILL CEASE

...With specific regard to the health situation [of your wife]:

It seems that this is mostly a case of nerves. Therefore, she should be inattentive to and unmindful of the entire matter, strengthening herself in her *bitachon* in the "Healer of all flesh, and Performer of wonders," the Creator and Director of the entire world.

[When your wife will do this,] the attacks — about which you write — will become more and more infrequent....

(Igros Kodesh, Vol. XII, p. 357)

"WORRY ABOUT WHY YOU ARE NEEDED, NOT ABOUT YOUR NEEDS"

In reply to your letter ... in which you write that you are very anxious and worried about your wife and family *sheyichyu*; also that you have grave concerns about earning a living, and consequently you do not have the peace of mind to engage in the study of G-d's Torah:

I am astonished that you completely fail to mention what you are doing regarding Torah and *mitzvos* in order to create vessels and channels through which to receive G-d's blessings regarding all the above [needs and concerns].

There is the famous saying of the Alter Rebbe, author of the *Tanya* (and [thus] *Posek* in the esoteric portion of Torah) and author of the *Shulchan Aruch* (and [thus] *Posek* in the exoteric portion of Torah), who replied to an individual who had a similar complaint: "Your concerns are all about what you need, but not what you are needed for."

The above is cited in a letter of my father-in-law, the Rebbe, of blessed memory, printed in *Kuntres 57*.[7] He mentions there as well that when one makes an effort to accomplish those things for which man was placed on earth — and as our Sages say at the conclusion of Tractate *Kiddushin*, "I was created for no other purpose than that of serving my Creator" — then G-d satisfies the person's needs and requirements.

(Igros Kodesh, Vol. VIII, p. 296)

COPING WITH NERVOUSNESS

You write about your being nervous:

It would be beneficial for you to study several chapters in *Shaar HaBitachon* in [the *Sefer*] *Chovos HaLevavos*.

Also, seek out those places in *Chassidus* that explain the concept mentioned in *Iggeres HaKodesh*, Epistle XXV, p. 138b: "Were he to believe that this came from G-d, etc."

From the above, it is obvious that there is nothing to be nervous about, as the pathways for drawing down G-d's blessings for all one's needs are known.

Moreover, these are well-trodden paths that each and every person is capable of treading confidently. By doing so, the person achieves self-elevation. Thus, there is no reason at all to be under constant nervous tension.

(Igros Kodesh, Vol. VIII, p. 279)

---

7   *Sefer HaMaamarim 5708*, p. 194.

WORRIES ABOUT DEPLETION
OF ONE'S NEST EGG

In reply to your letter of the 10th of *Menachem av*:

I am baffled by the statement in your letter that the difference [in your wealth] between last year and this year [is so great that it] defies the laws of nature — and in the phraseology of your letter you are not referring to [a difference on] the side of good, [but to the other side, due to the losses in your investment portfolio].

According to my thinking, if you will remind yourself about your current, [i.e., vastly improved,] state of health, and if you will consider that your wife is currently expecting a child in a good and auspicious hour, then it is abundantly clear that it indeed is, thank G-d, beyond the laws of nature — but to the side of good.

The fact of the matter is that for a short period of time the amounts that lie in your bank account have lessened, but this has caused no real loss in your actual standard of living, and surely has not affected you negatively in any of the three [critical] areas of children, life [and health,] and sustenance.

There is a popular saying from our Sages (*Sotah* 48b), that "he who has enough to sustain him for the day but is apprehensive about the morrow is considered to be wanting in faith."

This being so, [imagine how one should feel] when one — thank G-d — has enough cash to keep him going not only for the day but also for the month, and particularly when one has a sufficient reserve for the next several years but worries what [the situation] will be many more years in the future.

When the deposits in the bank become smaller, and consequently the anxiety about what will transpire many years in the future becomes ever greater, and one forgets at the time that [these losses] are truly incomparable to the goodness of improved health and the fulfillment of their wishes [for having a child] — this denotes an obscurity and concealment [of G-dliness and His bountiful blessings] to an extremely great degree.

Surely you understand that I am not stating the above as a reprimand. Only that it is a pity and it hurts to see a Jew who has so much to be joyful about — not only regarding spiritual matters but also regarding material matters, which is to say that the joy is then not only a soulful joy but a bodily joy as well, of both the Divine and animal soul. And instead of [focusing on] this [joy], you are worried and pained about what G-d — the One Who sustains all with kindness and mercy — will do several years from now with regard to your sustenance and the sustenance of your family.

As we now already find ourselves in the joyful days,[8] and according to the expression of the *Zohar* (*Yisro* 78b), that from the tenth of *Av* the forces of Esav, [i.e., the forces of evil,] vanish and are not to be found, so too should there be lost and never be found again all the concealments and smooth talk that stem from the side of Esav.

You will then see the fulfillment of serving G-d with "all your heart" (*b'chol levavcha*) and with a "complete heart" (*b'leivav shaleim*), [in both cases with the Hebrew spelling of the word "heart"] written with two "*veis*" letters, [signifying serving G-d with the completeness of the heart of the Divine soul as well as the heart of the animal soul] — so that you will serve G-d with joy.

(Igros Kodesh, Vol. IX, p. 242)

---

8   The letter was written on the 18th of *Av*, following the Three Weeks and the Ninth of *Av*.

OBTAINING RELIEF BY OCCUPYING ONE'S MIND WITH OTHER MATTERS

In reply to Monday's letter: As per your request, I will mention your wife ... in prayer at the holy resting place of my father-in-law, the Rebbe, of blessed memory, for a speedy recovery.

According to the way you describe the situation in your letter, it would seem that, in large part, your wife's pains stem from a case of nerves.

Thus, the more your wife will be inattentive and unmindful of this, [i.e., the thoughts that are troubling her,] by occupying her mind with other matters — and most importantly, the stronger her *bitachon* will be in G-d, "Healer of all flesh, and Performer of wonders," the more this will hasten her healing.

Understandably, this does not at all negate following the doctor's instructions, for "permission was granted to the healer to heal,"[9] and every matter has to be rooted in nature as well....

(Igros Kodesh, Vol. XI, p. 108)

DO NOT WORRY ABOUT WHAT IS IN G-D'S HANDS; CONCERN YOURSELF WITH WHAT IS IN YOUR HANDS

...You write about your current state of health and the illness you suffered in the past, and that the doctor told you that you must control your mental state and free yourself from worries, anxiety and stress:

---

9   *Berachos* 60a.

It is recognized that utilizing the attribute of *bitachon* is the best way to counter worry. The manner of generating this attribute within oneself is explained at length in many places [in our sacred writings], among them *Shaar HaBitachon* in *Sefer Chovos HaLevavos*.

In truth, this [attribute of *bitachon*] is a direct result of a foundation of the belief of the Jewish people — all of whom are "believers, sons of believers" — which is that G-d oversees each and every one of us with individual Divine providence, and that G-d is the Essence of Goodness. In the words of our Sages,[10] "All that G-d does, He does for the good."

In light of the above, what room can there possibly be for worry? It is only when one forgets a fundamental principle of faith that it is possible for one to worry."

It is worth noting that, in accordance with the above, this [aspect of not having to worry because matters are in G-d's benevolent hands] only applies to those things that are "in the hands of Heaven."

However, since our Sages say,[11] "Everything is in the hands of Heaven, except for the fear of Heaven," it follows that a person should be concerned with how he can improve his behavior so that it will be in concert with the words of the *Mishnah*:[12] "I was created to serve my Master...."

(Igros Kodesh, Vol. XVII, p. 100)

---

10   *Ibid.* 60b.

11   *Ibid.*, 33b.

12   *Kiddushin* 82a.

REMOVING WORRIES BY STUDYING CHAPTER TWENTY-THREE IN TEHILLIM

In reply to your letter ... in which you write that you find yourself constantly worrying:

I am indeed surprised that this is so, after your having merited to study for a lengthy period of time in the holy *Yeshivah* of *Tomchei Temimim* (and "Holiness is not subject to change"[13]), in which you studied [not only the exoteric portion of Torah, but] also *Chassidus*, which explains the theme of individual Divine providence and how G-d is the Essence of Goodness, and how "It is in the nature of He Who is good to do good," etc.

It would be beneficial for you to study chapter 23 of *Tehillim*[14] with many of the commentaries, and to review it from time to time.

It would also be proper for you to check your *tefillin* if they have not been checked in the past twelve months....

(Igros Kodesh, Vol. XXIII, p. 90)

OVERCOMING WORRYING THOUGHTS AND FEELINGS OF SADNESS

I received your letter in a timely fashion. However, I was not able to respond until now for any number of reasons. I hope that by the time you receive this letter your mental disposition will have improved.

---

13   See *Eitz Chayim, Shaar* 4:3; 34:3; *Shalah*, ch. 1; elucidation of *Iggeres HaKodesh,* Epistle XXVII.

14   The chapter that begins: "The L-rd is my shepherd, I shall lack nothing."

I am intentionally sending my response at the conclusion and termination of the month of *Nissan* (the month of freedom and liberation, including of course freedom from all disruptive thoughts and matters) and the time of preparation for the month of *Iyar*, known as the month of *Ziv* ("ray of light"), at which time — in accordance with the explanation of our Sages[15] — [sacred] rays of light and illumination are intensified within the world.

It is self-understood that my intent in the above words is that they address yourself — that now is a propitious time to increase G-d's blessings for success in all your matters, beginning with strengthening your physical health.

Doing something about it, [i.e., doing something concrete to bring about an improvement in your mental state,] (even if it be but a minor action), draws down from Above and increases G-d's blessings many more times so [than the person's action].

First and foremost of these actions is to strengthen one's *bitachon* in G-d and to contemplate G-d's Divine providence: how G-d oversees each and every individual, extending His providence to each and every detail within that individual's life.

The immediate [and obvious] conclusion from the above: do not pay attention to those thoughts that — G-d forbid — arouse worry or sadness. This is particularly so, according to that which is explained in *Toras HaChassidus* from our Rebbeim and *Nesi'im*, how sadness and melancholy should be utterly negated.

This negation is not to be accomplished through internal debate and bringing proofs, etc., [that such thoughts are wrong and harmful,] but by being completely inattentive and unmindful of these thoughts.

---

15   See *Rosh HaShanah* 11a.

Should you find it difficult to free yourself of these thoughts, one bit of sound advice is to alter your thoughts, occupying your mind with matters that have absolutely nothing at all to do with your previous [injurious] thoughts. Do not even negate the previous thoughts, just think about something completely different.

Additionally, since every matter must be rooted in nature as well, it would be appropriate for you to ask the opinion of a doctor [who specializes in this area] and follow his instructions. As to which doctor you should confer with — consult with your family doctor.

Do all the above with strong feelings of *bitachon* — in the words of King David, "Sweet Singer of Israel": "The L-rd is my shepherd, I shall lack nothing";[16] "The L-rd is with me, I do not fear."[17] May all the above be accomplished in good health and gladness of heart.

With blessings for good spirits and glad tidings regarding all the above, and with regards to your parents, *sheyichyu.*

P.S. As I want you to receive this letter while we are still in the month of *Nissan* or, at the latest, on *Rosh Chodesh Ziv*, I am therefore sending this letter by express mail.

(Igros Kodesh, Vol. XXIII, p. 158)

"YOU ARE WITH ME"

I received in a timely manner the *pidyon nefesh* [written] for you by ..., in which he writes that you are suffering from a certain fear:

---

16   *Tehillim* 23:1.

17   *Ibid.* 118:6.

I hereby want to emphasize [to you] once again that every Jew, both woman and man, should be strong in their *bitachon* in blessed G-d. Just as every Jew believes with complete faith that G-d is the Master of the world, so too is He the Master of the life of every individual Jew, male and female.

As it is a given that G-d is good, He will surely lead [matters in the direction of good and] to the good. And when people find themselves under the care — *hashgachah pratis* — of G-d, then there is nothing to fear. As King David says in *Tehillim*,[18] "I will fear no evil, for You are with me." This aspect of "You are with me" applies to each and every Jew.

(Igros Kodesh, Vol. V, p. 242)

SPIRITUAL AND PSYCHOLOGICAL ADVICE FOR COMBATING NIGHT TERRORS

...You write that you suffer from night terrors:

Check your *tefillin* and *mezuzos*; be even more scrupulous in your recitation of the bedtime *Shema* and while in bed verbally recite from memory or just think by heart several lines of *Tanya*. Study several times *Shaar HaBitachon* in the *Sefer* of *Chovos HaLevavos*.

Completely ignore and be heedless of these terrors — do not even fight them. They will of themselves become ever weaker; ultimately, you will be completely free of them.

Surely you have a pocket-sized picture of my father-in-law, the Rebbe.

(Igros Kodesh, Vol. XI, p. 162)

---

18   23:3.

NEGATING FEARS OF "EVIL SPIRITS"

In reply to your letter from the fourth of *Cheshvan*, in which you enclosed a *pidyon nefesh* on behalf of Mrs. ... *tichye*:

[Convey to her that] the *mezuzos* in her home should be checked to insure that they are all kosher according to Jewish Law. Before she goes to sleep, she should recite at least the first section of the bedtime *Shema,* and weekday mornings she should give several francs to *tzedakah.*

Additionally, [convey to her that] she should be completely unmindful and inattentive to all these groundless thoughts about "evil spirits" (*sheidim*) and the like.

It has already been stated,[19] "The Guardian of Israel neither slumbers nor sleeps," and it is also stated,[20] "He will cover you with His pinions [and you will find refuge under His wings]... You will not fear the terror of the night, etc. ... When he calls on Me, I will answer him, etc."

(Igros Kodesh, Vol. XII, p. 64)

FEAR OF BEING UNDER A MAGIC SPELL[21]

Explain to her the words of the [illustrious personage, the] *Rambam,*[22] [who states] that there is no reality to magic, etc.

(Neilchah B'Orchosov, p. 233)

---

19   *Tehillim* 121:4.

20   *Ibid.* 91:4,5,15.

21   The following is a response from the Rebbe regarding a woman who feared that she was being influenced by magic.

22   See *Rambam, Hilchos Akum* 11:16.

IMAGINED FEARS AND HEART PAIN

...Regarding that which you write about being fearful at times and that you also think you are suffering from a heart ailment:

In my opinion, both these matters are a fantasy. You should therefore examine your *tefillin*, as well as the *mezuzos* in your home — at the very least the *mezuzah* in your room; also check the *kashrus* of your *tallis kattan* on a daily basis.

Be strong in your *bitachon* that G-d, Who oversees every person with individual Divine providence, [constantly] hovers over you. Also, commit to memory the beginning of chapter 41 in the holy *Tanya*, at least until the word *haMelech* found at the beginning of p. 56b....

(Igros Kodesh, Vol. X, p. 289)

HEADACHES CAUSED BY NERVES

I received your *pidyon nefesh* in which you write that you are not feeling well, that you are suffering from headaches and the like. When I will be at the holy resting place of my father-in-law, the Rebbe, of sainted memory, I will remember you in prayer for good health.

Since in the majority of instances [symptoms such as yours] result from anxiety and nerves, you should strengthen your *bitachon* in G-d, Who created and conducts the world, and Who also directs the various aspects of your life.

You therefore need not be anxious and apprehensive, for He will surely lead you in the path of goodness, strengthening your health as well. The greater your *bitachon* in G-d, the more rapidly will be the realization of the above.

Understandably, you are to maintain your conduct in the paths of Torah and *mitzvos* and even increase your performance — that is to say, increase the amount you give to *tzedakah*, recite daily a chapter of *Tehillim*, and say a section of *Kerias Shema* before going to sleep.

It would also be advisable for you to check the *mezuzos* in your home to assure that they are all kosher.

(Igros Kodesh, Vol. VI, p. 94)

OVERCOMING ANXIETIES

It was upsetting not to have heard any news from you for such a long while. It therefore gladdened me greatly to receive your letter with the news that — thank G-d — your health has improved. Naturally I will read the *pidyon nefesh* that you sent at the sacred resting place of my father-in-law, the Rebbe.

Once again, I reiterate [my request] that you think long and hard about how G-d directs the world as a whole, and each and every one of us in particular.

Realizing this will remove your anxieties, for it will then be clear to you that G-d takes care of [all] matters in the best possible manner. Taking care, [i.e., micromanaging our lives in their every detail,] is not our responsibility; our responsibility is solely regarding matters of performing Torah and *mitzvos*, over which we were granted freedom of choice [and not over matters that are Divinely ordained and over which we do not have freedom of choice].

[With the above,] I am not writing anything new; these matters are basic and known to all. However, if these matters remain tangential [to our lives and we know them only peripherally,] and in actual practice we conduct ourselves as if these matters depend on ourselves, then we make our lives — our actual physical lives — extremely difficult.

This, however, is not the case when we are permeated with the concept that "G-d is my shepherd"[23] — then even the body and animal soul are cognizant that "I lack nothing."[24]

Heaven forfend that [you think] I am chastising you; it is only that I am pained by your anguish and distress which you cause yourself over something that has no foundation and surely is also groundless — and as known, the difference between the service of "tests" (nisyonos), [where the difficulty is merely in the person's own mind and once the person succeeds in overcoming the test, the difficulty disappears,] and the service of "refinement and elevation" (birurim).

Looking forward to hearing glad tidings from you about the improvement in your and your wife's health.

(Igros Kodesh, Vol. IV, p. 189)

CALM THE NERVES WITH A CALMING CHAPTER OF TEHILLIM

Study chapter 23 of *Tehillim*[25] until you are well versed in its content (not necessarily the exact words, and it makes no

---

23   *Tehillim* 23:1.

24   Conclusion of the above verse.

25   The chapter that begins: "The L-rd is my shepherd, I shall lack nothing."

difference in which language you study it).

Recite the above chapter [any time during the day] on *Shabbos* and Monday and Thursday, *bli neder*. Give several cents to charity on weekday mornings as well as before lighting candles *erev Shabbos* and *erev Yom Tov*, *bli neder*.

In the future, pay no attention *at all* if somebody speaks about you; don't ask them about this, [i.e., if they spoke about you,] at all. For (as stated in the above chapter [of *Tehillim*,] "G-d is with you" and "only goodness and kindness will follow you."

Consequently — no one at all can have power over you *at all*.

If your family doctor prescribes medication to calm you and the like, make sure to take it.

...Your husband should check his *tefillin* and the *mezuzos* in your home if they have not been checked in the past twelve months.

(Igros Kodesh, Vol. XXV, p. 256)

FEELINGS OF CONSTRICTION — A MATTER OF NERVES

In reply to your letter of the 10th of *Menachem* [*Av*,] in which you write that there are times when you feel a constriction in your windpipe:

This is merely a matter of nerves, from which we understand that if you take your mind off this matter and strengthen your *bitachon* in G-d, "Healer of all flesh and Performer of wonders,"[26] [i.e., the giver of the Torah and

---

26   After the text of the *Asher Yatzar* blessing.

its commandments,] then your symptoms will gradually disappear by themselves.

You must, however, provide at least some vessel via natural means [in which to receive G-d's healing]. You should therefore go to a doctor and follow his instructions.

Of course, you should also increase your diligence and assiduousness in your study of Torah, both *Toras HaNiglah* and *Toras HaChassidus*, and see to it that you affect your friends in this direction. [When you do so,] it will be good for you both materially and spiritually.

(Igros Kodesh, Vol. XV, p. 322)

GROUNDLESS WORRIES CAN DISAPPEAR OVERNIGHT WHEN WORRIES ARE NOT EGGED ON

I recently received your letter that came in response to mine. However, even in your second letter I fail to see any grounds for your lack of happiness and for that which you write that suddenly everything has fallen apart.

Since your lack of happiness is based on something without foundation, it can easily disappear — "here today and gone tomorrow" — that is, provided you do not egg it on by morose thoughts that are contrary to the nature of man and the dictates of our Torah of Life that requires us to serve G-d (service which can and must be during every moment of our lives) specifically with joy.

You surely know from your own experience, and we verily observe that if at times it is difficult to battle a certain mood, the best advice is to distract your attention from the situation not by fighting these thoughts, but by focusing your thoughts elsewhere.

The general catch-phrase for this is: "G-d made man uncomplicated, but *they* have sought many schemes."[27] Since it is "they," [i.e., the person himself and not G-d,] who is doing the scheming, therefore this can be easily nullified.

As per your request, when I am at the holy resting place of my father-in-law, the Rebbe, of sainted memory, I will mention in prayer all the individuals you wrote about.

I will conclude with my advice — since you sought my counsel:

Completely ignore all your introspective, self-examining thoughts and go forth with confidence along life's path, since G-d's providence accompanies all of us every step of our lives — not only regarding those matters that seem to us to be of great import, but in each and every detail of our lives. And, as known, this is one of the fundaments of the teachings of the Baal Shem Tov, later expounded upon at length in the teachings of *Chassidus Chabad*.

(Igros Kodesh, Vol. X, p. 118)

OVERCOMING INSECURITIES AND DIFFICULTIES IN MAKING DECISIONS

With reference to that which you write about your uncertainties and the difficulty in making decisions, as well as about general feelings of insecurity:

---

27   *Koheles* 7:29.

I trust it is unnecessary to elaborate to you at length that such feelings arise when a person thinks that he is alone and can rely only upon himself and his own judgment, and therefore feels doubtful and insecure about each move he has to make.

...However, when a person possesses a deep and abiding faith in G-d, and when he reflects that G-d's benevolent individual Divine providence extends each and every moment to each and every person and to each and every detail, he will surely develop a profound sense of security and confidence.

(From a letter of the Rebbe, dated 25 Elul, 5735)

REDUCING ANXIETY AND INCREASING PEACE OF MIND THROUGH BITACHON

...I trust you know that one of the basic tenets of our religion and way of life is to have complete *bitachon* in G-d, Whose benevolent providence extends to each and every one individually.

In addition to this being a must for its own sake, it will go a long way to reducing anxiety and strengthening your peace of mind.

At the same time, it is, of course, necessary to follow the instructions of one's doctor, which is also one of the teachings of our Torah.

May G-d grant that you should have good news to report in all the above....

(From a letter of the Rebbe, dated 10 Menachem Av, 5743)

chapter 4

ASSISTANCE IN DEALING WITH
VARIOUS MENTAL HEALTH ISSUES

FEELINGS OF PERSECUTION

You write that there are those who are hostile to you and your activities:

Be unmindful and inattentive to all this, for surely a large part of this [hostility and antagonism] exists only in your imagination. The remaining part can be nullified by [causing a reciprocal love within your antagonist, as the verse states:][1] "As water reflects the face, [so does one heart reflect the other."] You can do this, [i.e., bring about a reciprocal feeling within your antagonist,] by improving your relationship and treating that person in a more kindly manner....

(Igros Kodesh, Vol. XI, p. 162)

OVERCOMING PERSONAL PROBLEMS BY BEING IN THE COMPANY OF OTHERS

I received your letter of the 29th of *Adar*, and may G-d grant that you have good news to report on the matters about which you write in your letter.

...As for your personal problems, the best advice is that you should try to think as little as possible about your inner problems, until you completely dismiss them from your mind.

---

1   *Mishlei* 27:20.

This means that you should not even think about their harmful aspects or how to overcome them, but completely disengage yourself from these thoughts. Rather, engage your thoughts in matters of Torah and *mitzvos*.

Another good method [beneficial in overcoming personal problems] is to try to be in the company of other people as much as possible....

(From a letter of the Rebbe, dated 11 Nissan, 5720)

COMBATING FEELINGS OF LONELINESS

...As for your [gloomy] moods and feelings of loneliness, etc.:

Surely there is no room for such feelings in light of the teachings of the Baal Shem Tov regarding the true concept of Divine providence, which extends to each and every individual and to every aspect of life.

The realization of this [concept] must [inevitably and certainly] instill a deep feeling of confidence and optimism. You would do well to reflect upon this subject.

(From a letter of the Rebbe, dated "In the Days of Selichos," 5720)

ENHANCING A SENSE OF SELF BY ESTABLISHING A WORK ROUTINE AND KNOWING THAT HIS LOVED ONES HAVE CONFIDENCE IN HIM

Following the pleasure of our meeting and conversation after the *Farbrengen* last night, I wish to add here in writing some thoughts which, for obvious reasons, I did not wish to express in the presence of others, namely, in regard to your son.

I am in agreement with the opinion of your brother-in-law mentioned in your letter, especially as he is a physician. I believe that the best help that can be given your son, in general, is to get him to work.

I should only add, and I trust your brother-in-law would concur, that in view of the fact that this would entail a change in your son's way of life for a period of time, it would be well if his job would, in the first stage at any rate, meet two conditions:

Firstly, that it would not impose on him too much responsibility, so that he would not be frightened or discouraged by it.

On the other hand, it should have a more or less rigid timetable and schedule, so that he would get used to a routine and orderly life, which, in my opinion, is the overriding consideration.

If it is the kind of work which he might consider beneath him, it might be explained to him that it is only a start, and temporary, and, indeed, the first step to advancement.

It is well known that, here in the USA people at the top, often take pride in the fact that they worked their way up from the bottom of the ladder.

After he adjusts himself to a part-time occupation of several hours a day, he could probably be induced to work half a day and in due course a full-time job.

Needless to say, the above is in addition to what we spoke about the importance of his feeling that his parents and friends have the fullest confidence in him . . .

(From a letter of the Rebbe, dated 12 Nissan, 5734)

DISSATISFACTION WITH LIFE BECAUSE OF A LACK OF INNER PEACE AND TRANQUILITY

In reply to your two letters in which you write a synopsis of your life, your current frame of mind, and your general recent mental state, etc.

In general, it is not at all surprising for a Jewish man or woman to lack serenity and peace of mind if their daily conduct is not in keeping with their inner and essential nature, i.e., if they do not conduct themselves in accordance with the statement of our sacred Torah:[2] "You are children to the L-rd your G-d."

If an ordinary child must conduct himself according to the directives of his parents, how much more so — infinitely more so, in fact — with regard to G-d's children, Jewish sons and daughters, whose Father in Heaven taught them how to live their lives in accordance with His Torah (from the word "lesson"), which is called "the Torah of Life."

Moreover, G-d also created the Jewish people in a manner that their lives will be optimal when they lead such a life, [i.e., a life conducted according to the Torah]. Consequently, disruption of such a life, [i.e., conduct not in keeping with the Torah,] leads to a disruption of a person's state of serenity and contentment.

From the above, the main piece of advice for how you can rectify the situation [(and lead a happy life)] is eminently understandable: First and foremost, you must from now on conduct yourself in a manner that is consonant with the will of G-d — Creator and Director of man — as delineated in the Code of Jewish Law.

---

2   *Ibid.* 14:1.

Understandably, I assume that there are those who will question the above statement based on the fact that there are many individuals who do not perform *mitzvos* and nevertheless seemingly lead lives that lack for nothing, including no lack of tranquility, etc.

The answer to this question is simple as well:

a) One does not know what is in another person's heart — particularly regarding those areas where an individual will understandably be reluctant to reveal them to another.

b) This is similar to a person being, Heaven forbid, physically ill — the fact that someone who is ill may not be aware of his illness is not a sign of good health. To the contrary, it signals how ill that person really is; so too, and even more so, with regard to spiritual illness.

With regard to your request for practical advice, etc.:

According to the description in your letter [about the disarray and chaos in your life,] you should begin ordering your life in a manner which will enable you to get used to living an organized life on a daily basis.

Doing so will make it easier for you to enter into a routine and live an established course of life and provide you with self-discipline, with your mind and intellect controlling your heart and emotions, and so on.

Understandably, this does not in any way negate that which I wrote you in the beginning of the letter [about leading a life according to the directives of the Torah]. It is merely that within this [Torah] framework itself, [the Torah dictates that] a person is to do whatever he or she can via natural means [to attain better mental health].

It seems that one of the main contributing factors to your distressed mental state is your chaotic manner of living, with its lack of consistency in your ordinary everyday affairs. This [disorder and disarray] has a direct effect on your state of mind, your moods and feelings, etc.

It is of course difficult to suddenly become used to an organized and structured lifestyle after having lived a long time in a disorderly and chaotic manner.

One of the ways to make this easier is by having this [order and structure imposed on you] externally — by this I mean by taking a job and the like. This will trigger feelings of obligation in relation to others, [and having] the responsibility of a steady job with fixed hours.

Reading between the lines of your letter, you seem to feel that there are serious buried issues and the like [that are causing your problems]. However, in my opinion, the main point and crucial factor are the two matters I mentioned above: conducting your life in accordance with the Torah, and living an ordered and structured life.

When you rectify the above (little by little, at least), your situation will vastly improve, possibly becoming completely better.

Another point — and it, too, is crucial — is that you find an appropriate mate. Quite plainly, however, this matter can only be approached — and surely a final decision [as to whom you should marry] can only be made — in a tranquil state of mind, without turmoil.

Therefore, the first two matters [of conducting your life in accordance with the Torah, and living an ordered and structured life] take precedence, after which you should tackle the third issue: [interesting yourself in finding a *shidduch*].

It is difficult to estimate beforehand how much time is necessary to rectify the above [and return to a good state of mental health]. However, there is no doubt in my mind that all this depends on your staunch and unwavering desire and resolve to move in this direction. After this, [i.e., after having firmly resolved mentally to do so, you are] to implement this resolution with decisiveness and determination.

May G-d, who oversees each and every individual with His Divine providence, illuminate your path in life and grant you success in all your needs, materially and spiritually.

With blessings for spiritual and physical health, and may you be able to convey glad tidings [regarding the above].

(Igros Kodesh, Vol. XXIV, p. 178)

OVERCOMING CONSTANT DISSATISFACTION

...You write that you are dissatisfied with your work and that the work is difficult, etc.:

Although it flies in the face of common sense, there are many individuals who have resolved not to express joy and satisfaction at the way G-d conducts the world as a whole, and their lives in particular:

For, [were they to be satisfied and joyful with G-d's manner of conduct,] it could then possibly be construed that they are satisfied with their lot, when in point of fact their true feelings are that no matter how good things are for them, it is possible that things could be even better — which is why, [they feel,] they must constantly complain about their difficult lot in life and are invariably embittered about every facet and aspect of their lives.

Understandably, such conduct is contrary to the directives of our holy Torah. Surely it conflicts with the saying of our Sages[3] [in their comment] on the verse, "Let every being that has a soul praise G-d,"[4] that "one should praise G-d for his every breath."

...In addition to the above, the holy *Zohar* states[5] that presenting a melancholy countenance arouses — G-d forbid — a similar response from Above. However, when one is joyful and satisfied with his lot, no matter what his situation, this itself improves the situation, and matters go "from good to even better."...

(*Igros Kodesh, Vol. XI, p. 321*)

OPTIMISM AND PESSIMISM

It pleased me to receive your letter of 8/20 in which you write that you are feeling a little better; hopefully your health situation will go "from good to even better."

...I must, however, disagree with the statement in your letter that the grounds for viewing joyfully the events transpiring in the world at large, [as well as in one's personal world, are merely] to conceal the truth, [i.e., that matters are not all that joyous]. Rather, [viewing matters with a positive perspective and in a joyful light] is a means by which a person can make his life much more joyful and tranquil.

Furthermore, it is already well known, and medical science acknowledges this to an ever-greater extent, that the entire condition of the individual, [not only psychologically, but] physiologically as well, is impacted by the manner in

---

3   See *Bereishis Rabbah*, conclusion of ch. 14, and *Devarim Rabbah*, end of ch. 2.

4   *Tehillim* 150:6.

5   II, p. 184b.

which he perceives events surrounding him. This is to say that, to a large extent, the person's entire state depends on how he reacts to external and internal events.

Indeed, it is most significant that among the [philosophical] founders of the school of optimism, there were quite a number whose lives filled with experiences that we would term travails. Conversely, among the pessimists, we find many whose lives were abundantly good and were lacking nothing ... except for satisfaction and joy in their lives.

As I am aware of the experiences and events that transpired with your parents in their childhood, [and who nevertheless maintained their sense of optimism and joy in life,] this may possibly also serve — to a certain extent — as an example for you regarding the above.

It therefore is no wonder that *Chassidus*, which makes the most lofty and finest matters readily accessible to all, has as one of its fundamental concepts the notion that within each and every event that transpires in a person's life, there is a lesson to be learned in his Divine service.

This is in addition to the point stressed in *Chassidus* that service of G-d in general is to be performed with maximum joy, for only then is one's spiritual service in the greatest possible manner....

(Igros Kodesh, Vol. XI, p. 383)

OPTIMISM

The Rebbe often spoke of how optimism, reinforced by a trust in G-d, is just as important to the healing process as medicine and doctors. In 1977, the Rebbe suffered a serious heart attack.

One day later, he insisted on giving a talk as he had done on that
particular day for the previous 38 years.

"You must take care of your health," the doctor insisted. "If
not, there is a twenty-five percent chance of a relapse." The
doctor asked if the Rebbe understood what he had said. "Oh,
yes," said the Rebbe with a smile. "You said that even if I don't
take care of my health — which, I assure you, I will — there is
a seventy-five percent chance that there won't be a relapse."

HYPOCHONDRIA

...You write about your [supposed] various ailments:

Without a doubt, these [symptoms have no basis in
reality, but] are merely [a result of] *marah shechorah*, [an
inherent gloominess and a dark temperament that cause you
to imagine these things].

The counsel given in such an instance is known — in
accordance with that which is explained in the Alter Rebbe's
Torah Or, Parshas Toldos, an elucidation on the discourse
titled *Mayim Rabbim* — that it is appropriate to utilize one's
marah shechorah to increase one's diligence in Torah study.
Understandably, this should be accomplished in a manner
where it won't damage your health, G-d forbid....

(Igros Kodesh, Vol. III, p. 401)

ACHIEVING PEACE OF MIND

...Regarding your question, "What is peace of mind?," I am
not quite sure about the meaning of your query.

If your intent is, "How does one achieve peace of mind?," [then the answer is] that this depends on the degree and strength of one's *bitachon*, particularly according to the teaching of the Baal Shem Tov regarding individual Divine providence.

It would be worthwhile for you to study again and again the section of *Shaar HaBitachon* in the book *Chovos HaLevavos*....

(Igros Kodesh, Vol. XV, p. 295)

OVERCOMING LONELINESS

In reply to your letter in which you write that you have been studying in Seminary for some time and nonetheless you are unable to make friends among your fellow students; you thus find yourself isolated — something that understandably has an effect on your spirits, etc.:

You should seek the counsel of your teachers as to which of the girls would be best to have as friends and then make an effort to seek out their friendship.

A general piece of advice about reducing one's isolation: Contemplate the fact that there is no person in the world who is absolutely perfect, yourself included, which is to say, that you yourself are also imperfect and you should not require and demand to see all these sterling qualities and aspects in another [before you become friendly with them].

Moreover, our Sages, of blessed memory, have testified, "all Jewish daughters are beautiful;" each one of them is deemed "a daughter of Sarah, Rivkah, Rachel and Leah." Surely you possess very many good qualities and, with the passage of time, you will come to recognize them. Moreover, becoming friendly with others will serve to reveal your [good] qualities as well.

The more you contemplate the above points, the easier it will be for you to obtain friends, and the quicker your loneliness and isolation will dissipate — and in the memorable words of our Sages, of blessed memory:[6] "Acquire for yourself a friend."

(Igros Kodesh, Vol. XVIII, p. 323)

DEALING WITH LONELINESS

I would like to confirm receipt of your letter — undated — in which you write about your emotional state etc.

I believe that I have previously written a few times, that in my opinion — and this is what I have clearly seen in actuality — every person, without exception, has a natural need for social contact, though obviously the level of dependency varies from person to person. When one tries to ignore this natural need it understandably brings to "complications" and the like. For those who for some reason have difficulty connecting with others, their only solution is as in the case of learning how to swim, which is impossible before entering the water, even when standing close to the edge of the river. Rather, one must first jump into the water. Automatically, the process of gaining swimming skills begins and eventually one masters them. Contemplating whilst standing at the edge of the river how, what, and in which manner he will learn to swim, is useless; as it is impossible to learn how to swim unless one is in water.

---

6   *Avos* 1:6.

Pardon me for saying so, but this is the case in your regard. In your letter you argue whether or not to accept a job which will involve being in the presence and company of others, all whilst sitting in your own room or personal space.

Obviously I do not intend to admonish, rather to try once more; possibly, this time my words will be effective and you will "jump in" to a situation in which you will be forced (at least for the first few days) to be amongst people outside of your own home, and I strongly hope that within a short amount of time it will no longer be a strain and you will see the great importance and gain, also for others in society, as it is not for naught that man was created with a natural need for social contact.

How amazing are the words of our sages, which are a practical guide for day to day life, that any matter of holiness should be conducted in the presence of ten people, not only publicly but the complete form of public. There is also a known Chassidic saying repeated in the name of great Chassidic masters, that it is worse [to be] in Gan Eden all alone then to be in... with the company of other Jews.

...May it be the will of G-d that there be drastic development for the good and that you will have good news in this area.

With blessings for good news....

(Igros Kodesh, Vol. XVIII, p. 534)

MAKING RESOLUTIONS STICK

In reply to your letter of the 19th of *Menachem Av* in which you ask for advice about your lack of orderliness: you decide to conduct yourself in a specific manner but it does not last and you revert to your previous mode of conduct. [You also write that] the above [manner of conduct] is disruptive to both you and others:

Quite often, this results from resolving to do things that are distant and far removed from your present level, which is to say, you desire to "jump" when the normal course of action is to improve little by little, step by step.

{There are, in fact, unusual circumstances when the [most appropriate] course of action is one of "jumping" and "leaping": going from one extreme to the other in one fell swoop. However, this is not the usual manner of conduct [where one seeks to achieve incremental progress].}

Another piece of advice that will enable your resolutions to endure is that of sharing your resolve with a friend. This makes it difficult not to continue following the resolution, since you would have to answer to your friend for not doing so.

(Igros Kodesh, Vol. XX, p. 311)

INABILITY TO CONCENTRATE

...Regarding that which you write about your [difficulty in] concentrating:

There is the known counsel of studying while gazing in the book [from which you are studying] and praying from a prayer book. The book should be open in front of you at the place where you are holding in your studies, even when you are studying by heart or engrossed in thought.

(Igros Kodesh, Vol. XVII, p. 331)

DON'T FORCE YOUR CONTINUED CONCENTRATION ON A SUBJECT YOU GREW TIRED OF

...With regard to that which you write about your weak power of concentration:

One of the proven pieces of advice regarding this matter is that when becoming tired [of thinking about one area of learning and study], then shift to some other area of study — whatever your heart desires. Do not force your power of thought to concentrate specifically about something that has already tired you out....

(Igros Kodesh, Vol. IX, p. 90)

When your studies begin to tire you, [i.e., your concentration begins to wane,] and your head begins to ache, you should change the subject matter to another area of Torah, from study that requires depth and intensity (*l'iyuna*) to a less intensive and exhaustive subject of study (*l'migras*) — from *Halachah* to *Aggadah* and the like — for *approximately* an hour.

Such [difficulties in studying and concentration] are extremely common to *many* and should be absolutely no cause for concern.

[You should also] check your *tefillin* and assure that your *tallis kattan* is kosher.

(From a handwritten response of the Rebbe)

FLUCTUATIONS IN MOOD, SELF-CONFIDENCE AND POWER OF CONCENTRATION

...It is also self-understood that all of us, as members of the human race, are not always in the same mood — for which reason man is in a state of flux between ascent and descent.

Even the greatest of the great, the truly, completely righteous (*tzaddikim gemurim amiti'im*) — [and by this I mean that] they are on the level [of *tzaddikim gemurim*] as described by the Alter Rebbe [in *Tanya*] — nevertheless, he explains[7] that the verse[8] "For a *tzaddik* may fall seven times, yet rises again" applies even to them; it is only that regarding a *tzaddik*, his "fall" is only in comparison to his previous state, etc.

From the above, it is understood that it is quite normal for you to not always be able to concentrate to the same extent, and so too with regard to self-confidence, etc.

This is particularly so when, in addition to all the above, there are the added machinations of the evil inclination, who [greatly exaggerates those matters about which you are self-critical, since he] desires to hinder man's service of his Creator, and one of the foundations of this service is an utterly tranquil mental state and complete *bitachon* that "All G-d does, He does for the good."...

(Igros Kodesh, Vol. XIX, p. 106)

---

7   *Tanya*, p. 76a.

8   *Mishlei* 24:16.

WHEN ONE'S HOME EVOKES SAD MEMORIES

...You write about moving. ...This is not advisable at the present time.

As to the fact that your present dwelling evokes [depressing] memories: It may be beneficial to change around the furniture, or even the use of the rooms, and the like.

Additionally, it would be proper, if at all possible, that from time to time there should be a Torah class in your house (at least with several people) whether in the revealed portion of Torah, or in the esoteric portion of Torah, which in our generations has been revealed in *Toras HaChassidus* — or in both together.

May you convey glad tidings regarding all the above.

(Igros Kodesh, Vol. XX, p. 128)

OVERCOMING EMOTIONAL TURMOIL AND FEELINGS OF DISSATISFACTION

You write that you find yourself in great emotional turmoil and that you find no gratification in your work, and moreover, you do not know how to overcome this:

Such emotional upsets are fully discussed in *Chassidus*, and even secular science has given much attention lately to what is called the subconscious.

A person may not be consciously aware of his true spiritual state and what he lacks — having suppressed certain inner drives — so that all he is aware of is a feeling of frustration and lack of self-fulfillment.

I refer, of course, to the fact that the Jew always has an inner drive to express his Divine soul. Those who are in a position of influence have an inner urge to exercise this influence to the utmost possible degree, to bring their fellow-Jews closer to our Torah, closer to the tradition of their fathers and to the Jewish way of life.

The fact that one becomes superficially absorbed in some activity which only resembles that of true Jewish education, or a religious activity which stresses the Jewish heart, and rightly so, but neglects to vigorously stress the real essence of Judaism, the daily performance of the *mitzvos*, to the extent that religion becomes a three-day affair or a matter of *yartzeit* services, etc., such activities do not provide real fulfillment for the soul, and, hence the inner urge is not fulfilled.

No doubt you have heard the explanation of the Alter Rebbe, [Rabbi Shneur Zalman, founder of Chabad,] when he was asked by a gentile scholar, what is the meaning of [the Torah verse,] "Where are you?," which G-d asked Adam; surely nothing is hidden from G-d.

The Alter Rebbe then replied that when Adam committed the sin [of eating from the Tree of Knowledge], he experienced a Divine call demanding, "Where are you? Do you realize what you have done and what you are supposed to do?"

The question "Where are you?," is always asked of every individual, especially the Jew, who has been endowed with a Divine soul. It calls for introspection and soul-searching in order to find one's self again.

It is clear from the above that it is quite unjustified to think that you have permanently lost contact, etc. G-d does not demand the impossible, and having set forth a program and a goal, He has simultaneously given the full ability and capacity to fulfill them.

It is only that G-d wants everyone to fulfill his purpose in life out of his own free choice, in spite of temptations and difficulties. If you will, therefore, realize that you have it in your power to overcome them, you will find yourself again and the context that you are missing at present.

(From a letter of the Rebbe)

OVERCOMING SELF-DOUBT AND DIFFICULTY IN MAKING DECISIONS

You write of your state of mind — that you find it difficult to make decisions on any matter and remain in constant doubt as to whether you are acting correctly and so on.

In view of your upbringing, of which you write, there is certainly no need for me to emphasize the subject of Divine providence, a fundamental principle in our faith and in our Torah, "the Torah of Life."

The meaning of this concept, *hashgachah pratis,* is straightforward — that G-d, Who created and directs the world, watches over every man and woman, not only in public matters but also in his private affairs. This concept enables us to understand the principle of trusting in the One Who conducts the world and Who is the Essence of Goodness, for accordingly, everything is also for the good, plainly and simply.

Every believer's mind, too, understands that the first direct result of this trust is that there is no worry and no confusion. For when a person is weighing in his mind what he should decide and how he should act, at that time, too, G-d is watching over him and helping him, helping all those who desire what is good and upright.

When one conducts himself according to the directives of the Torah, this is the good path, and such conduct in itself helps a person to proceed with all his affairs in a way that is good for him.

As in all matters of faith, the above-mentioned principle likewise requires neither intellectual arguments nor profound and complex philosophical proofs. For every individual of the Children of Israel, man or woman, senses in his soul that he truly has faith — even when he is not thinking about whether this principle is correct or whether it is a rational imperative.

As the Sages affirm, all Jews are "believers, sons of believers."[9] This means that the faith that is within them, both in their own right and as a heritage from their forebears who were believers, and all the spiritual properties [such as faith and love and fear of G-d] that became theirs in their own right and also as a heritage — this faith and these spiritual properties are supremely strong within them all. This is self-explanatory.

I hope that these lines of mine, limited as they are in quantity, will suffice to rouse your thoughts and guide you toward the truest and innermost point within your own self — that in your innermost soul you most definitely trust that G-d watches over you.

All you need to do is bring forth this thought from within your soul to your day-to-day life. After all, "There is nothing that stands in the way of the will."[10]

As was said above, the way to accomplish this is not by

---

9   In the original, *maaminim bnei maaminim* (*Shabbos* 97a).

10   This translates the universally cited Hebrew paraphrase of a teaching in *Zohar* II, p. 162b.

profound intellectual debate, but by relying on your inner feeling that you place your trust in G-d — not by seeking out doubts, nor by creating problematic queries that are not at all problematic and, in fact, do not trouble you.

Averting your attention from all of this will no doubt help you rid yourself easily of all the confusing factors that have been spoken of.

It would be advisable that before the morning prayers on weekdays, a few times a week, you set aside a few cents to be donated for *tzedakah* — preferably on Mondays and Thursdays and on *erev Shabbos*. And it goes without saying that such an undertaking should be made without a formal vow.[11]

With blessings for a strengthening of your *bitachon* and for good news regarding all the above....

(Igros Kodesh, Vol. XVIII, p. 408)

LIVE LIFE SIMPLY AND WITHOUT COMPLICATION; CEASE YOUR INCESSANT SELF-EXAMINATION

...It would be most beneficial that for about a year you entirely cease dwelling on making an "accounting" of your life: how others treat you, your relationship to the entire world, etc.

Perform with simplicity that which our Torah states,[12] "Serve G-d in a wholehearted manner, [i.e., without pretentiousness] — living the life of the "mainstay of the household" in an uncomplicated and artless manner:

---

11   In the original, *bli neder.*

12   *Devarim* 18:13.

[Occupy yourself in seeing to] the *kashrus* of food and drink, *taharas hamishpachah*, receiving guests, the lessons of *Chitas,* and so on. And as mentioned above, do so in an utterly simple and unpretentious manner.

When you begin thinking "soul-searching thoughts," tell yourself decisively and purposefully that you refuse to think about these matters before the year 5748[13] — [and that you re-affirm to yourself that] presently my task is that my home and life be conducted with simplicity, wholeheartedness, and joy.

(Likkutei Sichos, Vol. XXXIV, p. 285)

OVERCOMING FEELINGS OF DEPRESSION CAUSED BY A SEEMING LACK OF SUCCESS

I received your letter of the 18th of *Menachem Av*, and, as you requested, I will remember you and all those mentioned in your letter in prayer when visiting the holy resting place of my father-in-law, of saintly memory.

You write that you feel depressed, as it appears to you that you have not succeeded in your studies at the *yeshivah* to the degree that you had expected.

Even assuming that you are completely correct in your appraisal, this still would be no reason for feeling depressed. For, as explained in many sources, particularly in the Book of *Tanya*, even in the case of spiritual failure, no Jew should feel depressed, as feelings of depression and gloom are

---

13   I.e., not before a little over a year's time, as the Rebbe's letter to this individual was dated 20 *Elul*, 5746, near the conclusion of the year 5746.

themselves one of the strategic weapons employed by the evil inclination in its efforts to discourage a person from serving G-d with joy and alacrity.

And, when the evil inclination succeeds in one thing, such as in discouraging you from study, as you write, he then goes on to other things.

The way to combat the evil inclination is, as explained in *Tanya*, to call forth redoubled effort on one's part to overcome the feelings of depression and replace them with a feeling of joy in the realization that no matter what the past has been, it is always possible to attach oneself to G-d through the study of the Torah and the observance of the *mitzvos*.

...In the final analysis, it is up to a person to overcome his difficulties through his own efforts and determination, and we have already been assured that where there is a determined effort, success is certain.

Moreover, in your case, it is quite possible that you have underestimated your success, a thought that could also have been implanted by the evil inclination in your mind.

(From a letter of the Rebbe, dated 25 *Menachem Av*, 5718)

OVERCOMING A PERSECUTION COMPLEX

...Needless to say, every additional measure of trust in G-d, and all additional efforts in performing Torah and *mitzvos* with joy and gladness of heart will increase your personal contentment, as well as the success of your activities on behalf of others.

This will also help you to realize the incongruity of your writing that everybody seems to be against you, something that cannot be true, in view of the fact that our Sages teach, "All that G-d does, He does for the good."[14]And when we speak of "good," we do not mean only the good in the hereafter, but in the here and now....

(From a letter of the Rebbe, dated 5 Iyar, 5721)

OVERCOMING PSYCHOLOGICAL PROBLEMS PARTIALLY DUE TO IMMATURITY[15]

(1) From time to time, and repeatedly so, make an effort to better the situation, with the assistance of a psychologist and medication.

Most importantly, your husband desires this as well, [i.e., that the marriage last,] for it is to his benefit (even in his view) and the benefit of the children *sheyichyu.*

The more your husband matures, the more the excess intensity and fervor of the days of his youth will subside, and his rational self will achieve greater dominance.

Thus, after *many, many* years of finding yourself in such a situation, surely the misery of the situation has lessened and is not as great as it was in the beginning.

(2) [A divorce] would mean the destruction, G-d forbid, of

---

14   *Berachos* 60b.

15   A woman who was having severe difficulties in keeping her marriage intact because of her husband's psychological problems inquired of the Rebbe whether to try to keep the family together, or whether to try to build a new life. The above is the Rebbe's response, dated *Isru Chag HaPesach*, 5747. The Rebbe responded with the following three points:

all that presently exists and the beginning of a new search for a new manner of life for yourself and your children (accompanied by the never-ending doubt as to whether you did the correct thing by destroying [the marriage], or whether you lost the chance [to rectify the situation]).

(3) Our Sages declare that "Great is peace," and that "the Divine Presence resides in a couple's midst,"[16] etc. Understandably, then, you should make the effort [to achieve peace and harmony in your marriage].

I will mention you in prayer at the holy resting site of my father-in-law, the Rebbe.

(Likkutei Sichos, Vol. XXXIX, p. 324)

OVERCOMING FEELINGS OF BEING IGNORED AND UNAPPRECIATED

...You go on at length about past events in your life, the disappointment that there were those who should have come to your aid but did not do so at all, etc.:

You fail, however, to mention even one word about what you have actually done for the welfare of anybody else throughout your entire life.

What seems to be even more alarming is that implicit in the tone of your letter is an utter absence of the notion that possibly you have an obligation to *actually* help others (not merely to have good intentions, or utter fine words, or to protest against those matters that you have absolutely no chance of changing, and the like).

---

16   *Sotah* 17a.

On the other hand, you are so absolutely certain that all that was done for you from the time you were born until the present was surely owed you, and that all this goodness [done for you by others, and which you so conveniently ignore,] in no way obligates you to stop thinking about your selfish desires.

[Moreover, you utterly fail to realize that this goodness that has been shown to you] necessitates that you use the required amount of effort to increase goodness and holiness to those in your surroundings to the greatest degree possible (thereby providing it as well to all who have been of assistance to you)....

(Likkutei Sichos, Vol. XXXVIII, p. 173)

CONSIDERATION AND ATTENTIVENESS TO ONE'S WIFE OFTEN RESULTS IN HER IMPROVED HEALTH

In many instances similar to your wife's, when the husband is more considerate and attentive to his wife, this results in an improvement in her health, etc.

Understandably, [I am referring to] an addition [of consideration and attentiveness] that she will be aware of and feel.

(Igros Kodesh, Vol. XXIV, p. 9)

In reply to the above response of the Rebbe, the recipient replied that he had already undertaken measures and was continuing to undertake measures to be considerate and attentive.

To this the Rebbe replied:

Regarding that which you write about the various acts of consideration and attentiveness that you have shown your wife [in the past] (and [continue to do so] in the present as well):

You are surely correct regarding the reckoning itself; however, in the present circumstances an additional and crucial aspect should be considered:

Your attentiveness and concern is of crucial import in terms of its healing properties (of both body and spirit), for which reason its effectiveness is expressly measured by its therapeutic effects, [and if these effects are lacking, then you have yet to accomplish the desired goal].

(This is in addition to the fact that in general, matters of the heart, [i.e., truly caring, etc.,] and [making] an accounting [of specific actions which show your care and concern], are not that much in harmony.) Surely to someone like you, a lengthy exposition is unnecessary.

May the Healer of all flesh grant your wife a full and speedy recovery.

(Igros Kodesh, Vol. XXIV, p. 109)

REGAINING ONE'S JOY IN LIFE BY ASSISTING OTHERS

Many other individuals whose lives were similar to yours (with regard to suffering, etc.), found relief when they devoted their energy and time and displayed genuine kindness and concern in an effort to assist others who found themselves in dire straits or in a state of confusion — doing so on a regular basis and as part of their ongoing daily schedule.

(From a letter of the Rebbe in the year 5730)

PEACE OF MIND
BEFORE DECIDING ON SURGERY

...P.S. After writing the above, I received your notification by telephone regarding the course of treatment that your doctors have suggested, and you ask my advice:

As known, one of the most important factors in [healing] ulcers is tranquility and peace of mind — something that depends almost entirely on the patient.

I therefore suggest that you strengthen your *bitachon* in G-d, the "Healer of all flesh and Performer of wonders."[17] You can accomplish this by reading and then pondering deeply selected selections [of books] that deal with this subject, such as the [section entitled] *Shaar HaBitachon* in the book *Chovos HaLevavos* (from Rabbeinu Bachya ibin Pekudah) and the like.

Additionally, it is well established that a proper diet is effective in such an instance, [i.e., in helping heal an ulcer]; I believe it is effective in all instances [of an ulcer], the difference being only in its degree of efficacy.

Therefore, since your situation has been ongoing for some time and the surgery is not urgent, I would suggest that you first try the two solutions mentioned above and see to what degree they ease the situation.

In any event, the auspicious time of the month of *Adar*

---

17   From the text of the *Asher Yatzar* blessing, from *Berachos* 60b.

begins in only three weeks. During that time you can assess the results of the two methods suggested above, after which you should again consult with your doctors.

In order to minimize your worries as quickly as possible, I am sending this letter via Special Delivery.

(From a letter of the Rebbe)

chapter 5

SPECIFIC TREATMENTS AND APPROACHES TO MENTAL HEALTH ISSUES AND PROBLEMS

OBSESSIVE-COMPULSIVE DISORDER

Your doctor has surely informed you that numerous individuals find themselves in the same situation that you describe (imagining that they did something imperfectly; that their hands are not clean, [i.e., ritualized hand washing,] for which reason they must wash their hands again, etc.).

When one makes a concentrated effort to be inattentive to these thoughts (not fighting these thoughts but being unmindful of them to the greatest possible degree), then [such thoughts] will dissipate with the passage of time, eventually disappearing entirely.

For example, when you desire to [re]wash your hands, do not make an issue of it. Rather, either say to yourself that this thought is insignificant and meaningless, [and pay the thought no heed,] or do wash your hands and then immediately occupy yourself with something that has absolutely no connection to your prior act [of washing your hands].

One's frail general health also serves as one of the causes for this disorder. Strengthening your general health will thus be of additional assistance in easing your condition.

Also, in order to hasten your healing, you should consult with a doctor who is also a friend and follow the doctor's directives.

Inspect the *mezuzos* [in your home to insure that they are all kosher according to Jewish Law].

Please convey your name and your mother's name to me

so that I may mention you in prayer at the holy resting place of my father-in-law, the Rebbe, of blessed memory, [for a full and speedy recovery].

(From a handwritten response of the Rebbe, circa 1973)

ADVICE ON CONQUERING ALCOHOLISM

In reply to your letter of *Teves* 24 in which you write about your good resolution [to stop drinking] after you received my previous letter, and that, after a period of time you were unable to withstand the test, etc.

The words of our Sages are known regarding such situations, that a person should not be crestfallen if he could not withstand a test and fell through. Surely this should not lead to hopelessness, Heaven forfend, in your battle with your evil inclination. To the contrary, hopelessness and dejection are the weapons used by the evil inclination. It says to man — to Israel, (the people who are close to Him;) "you are called man", each of them being a descendent of the Patriarchs, Avrohom, Yitzchak and Yaakov — to cease battling him, [for you see that you have previously failed, hence surely] "you will not be successful" etc. [in the future as well].

To the contrary. If you fell through and realize how abhorrent and bitter it was to fall through; not only was this opposite the will of the Creator, the Giver of the Torah and the Commander of the *mitzvos,* but it also led to destruction and devastation of one's physical life in this world, this should empower you to a greater and fiercer degree to stand fast in your abovementioned battle [with the evil inclination]. Ultimately, the promise that "If a man sanctifies himself somewhat below he will be sanctified a great deal from Above" will come to fruition.

A) In order to strengthen yourself in the above battle and hasten your victory, it would be most appropriate that you only carry around enough money to purchase minor items and the like.

B) To the greatest extent possible, see that you find yourself only in the company of people who observe Torah and *mitzvos*. Particularly so, since every Jew is so commanded, in line with our Sages' teaching, "Much [sinful] behavior is a result of [bad] friends," while "It is good for the righteous; it is good for his neighbor," with the opposite being the case as well.

C) Since many physicians are aware of medications that help a person overcome and conquer one's desire for such strong drink and with the passage of time to totally end such desire, you should ask them about this and follow their directives. It is also must crucial that you know by heart several chapters of *Mishnayos* and *Tehillim* and review them from time to time. Particularly so, when you are under the impression that you have such a desire....

(Igros Kodesh, Vol. 22, p. 110ff.)

IRREGULAR ATTRACTION

People are born with *diverse* natures, and education is *always* necessary to set the person properly on his/her feet. This applies to the training of good traits as well as the modification of bad traits.

Good tendencies in children must also be nurtured, directed and cultivated through proper education and training, for if not, the uneducated intellect can run amok and go against its own *good* nature. His actual conduct will not match his good tendencies.

When a child has character traits that are abnormal and undesirable, it is certainly the responsibility of the parents and teacher — those who love and really care for the child — to train the child and modify his/her attributes.

It is also self-evident that the behavior modification must be followed through, despite the objections and arguments of the child that this trait is: (a) part of his "nature," or (b) that he is willing to suffer the consequences, or, (c) that there will be no negative results of his actions. The necessary forcefulness must obviously be applied to be successful.

All this holds true in the normal course of growing up — evaluating and distinguishing the good and bad traits, and guiding the growth and maturity of the child.

There are times, however, when a child is born with a genetic deviation or deficiency, for example some emotional or mental disorders which have symptoms such as "tearing out their own hair," "[excessive] nail biting," "knocking their heads against a wall," or some other self-destructive traits.

It goes without saying that one who loves and cares for this child will do all he/she can to correct this aberrant behavior and seek a training plan, a learning module, or an educational framework to cure this deviation.

When the child grows up and is cured, he will surely feel a sense of gratitude to the ones who had "not spared the rod" of education and had pulled out all the stops to correct his deficiencies.

These universal principles of education as applied to children may also be adapted when we speak of rehabilitating adults. They, too, can be educated to modify their harmful traits and they, too, will be *eternally grateful* for such vitally important *help.*

Every person has the ability to choose "life." For some it is easier and for others it is harder, but without a doubt, if one so wills, he can overcome those traits which are offensive or self-destructive.

Educators, therapists and counselors should keep in mind that the possibility exists to eventually correct the problems, even though the troubled client might vehemently claim (which might actually be quite true) that his deviations are inborn and part of his nature.

They can be helped; and experience has shown that in the end they will express their eternal gratitude for the firm direction and support they received from family, counselors and friends.

Maimonides teaches:

Free will is bestowed on every human being. If one desires to turn towards the good way and be righteous, he has the power to do so. If one wishes to turn towards the evil way and be wicked, he is at liberty to do so (Laws of Repentance 5:1).

Consequently this true free will, described by Maimonides, is decisively all-powerful. Yet, in the laws relating to "Moral Disposition and Ethical Conduct," Maimonides admits that:

Every human being is characterized by numerous and exceedingly divergent moral dispositions ... One man is choleric, always hot tempered; another sedate, never angry ... one is a sensualist whose lusts are never gratified; another is so pure that he does not even long for the few things that our physical nature needs ... [Then there are those who are by nature] stingy, generous, cruel, merciful, and so forth. (Laws of Ethical Conduct 1:1)

Maimonides adds:

Of all the various dispositions, some belong to a person from the beginning of his existence and correspond to his physical constitution. (*Ibid.* 2)

In other words, some people are *born* with the nature of stinginess, etc., and others are born with different natures! Does everyone really have free will to freely choose right from wrong even if it seems to be against his/her nature?!

The commentaries on Maimonides explain that he means to say that although one may truly have an *inclination* and leaning *by his very nature,* and although he may show a propensity for certain conduct, none of these factors can *"force"* him to act in a particular way. He still has an absolutely free will!

The ideal way to control and overcome the offensive predispositions is to be trained, while still a child, by the strong and firm controlling hand of the loving parent and educator. But it is never too late for this educational process *to begin;* a human being can always learn, improve and progress.

At this point let us turn our attention to a phenomenon affecting some of our society, the problem of individuals who express an inclination towards a particular form of physical relationship in which the libidinal gratification is sought with members of one's own gender.

Empirical truth has shown us that this form of abnormal relationships has been totally negative.

1) In a normal relationship, the results which follow bring forth children and create a new generation, which goes on to bring future generations, to the end of time. The abnormal trait brings no positive results and no offspring.

2) This trait is self-debilitating. It causes a dissipation of the strength of the individuals involved, is purely selfish, and no one else receives anything from it.

3) Another very important reality: the individuals who practice this form of relationship are filled with the self-abnegating feeling of being strange and queer; they feel that they are doing an abnormal act.

Both in the case of men who have these relations, and in the case of women, they know that this tendency is not normal. They look at the world around them and they know that their practice is abnormal.

Except for a very few "orders" where this deviation is practiced, the *whole world conducts* itself in a *normal way*. Besides, both parties involved in this said relationship know that it was only the *normal* form of *family relationship* that brought them into the world!

4) Also important: Those who feel that this form of conduct is permissible and they continue to practice this deviation, will in the end see that it brings to excessive, abnormal weakness and the most horrible diseases and maladies, as we are presently *beginning* to discover.

When one knows the truth, that this trait is destructive, and is honest enough to acknowledge this fact, one will realize that it is no different from a child who is born with the tendency to tear out his hair, or bang his head against the wall.

But there is a very tragic difference in that when this trait is practiced, it is very much more devastating because it *destroys* the body and the soul.

There are those who argue that an act which brings pleasure and gratification is, or even *must* be, good. This rationalization is analogous to taking a deathly poison and coating it with sugar. Along comes someone and says, "I see *sugar,* there is no poison in this sugar pill." To prove his words, he tastes it and swears it is sweet!

Someone else may come along and say, "I don't care if there is *poison* in the sugar. So long as I can enjoy the momentary pleasure of the sweetness, albeit in an abnormal fashion, I don't care what the consequences will be!"

Certainly, *they themselves will* eventually complain very strongly against those who misled them, and also against those who saw what was going on and did not do *all* that was possible for them to do to prevent it from happening.

It makes no real difference what causes an individual to presently choose this form of relationship.

Even one who was *born* with this inclination and was not educated in his youth to correct it (no matter who is to blame) and is now an adult, must also be motivated to educate him/herself now, for it is still just as destructive; it is still just as abnormal, etc.

An important point to stress is that there *is no insult intended* and *no derogatory attitude* suggested; it is a case of *healing* a malady. When a person is ill and someone volunteers to help him get well, there is no disrespect involved, not at all!

At the same time, we must keep in mind that the vehement and vociferous arguments presented by a patient — that he is really well and that his condition is a healthy instinct, or at least not destructive — do not change the severity of the "ailment."

In fact, this attitude on the part of this individual indicates how serious his malady really is, how deeply it has penetrated into his body and psyche, and how perilous it really is for him.

And so, special action must be undertaken to heal the

person and save his life. And again, there is no insult at all and no disrespect involved; only a true desire to really help.

If he claims that he was born with this nature, this is indeed all the more reason to reassure him that no disparagement was meant, for it is no different from the case of one who was born with the tendency to bang his head against the wall. Do we shame that unfortunate one?! Nevertheless, everything must be done to remedy the situation.

And dubbing the deviation with some Greek term, or calling it an "alternative lifestyle" will not in the least influence the seriousness of the problem.

The question must be answered: Does this type of relationship contribute to human civilization? Does it, at least, benefit the individual? Is it truly *satisfying after* the act? Or, does it *only provide momentary* gratification?

And furthermore — this point should be carefully pursued — are all his/her protests about the "great pleasure" and "satisfaction" derived from this relationship really *true?* Or, has he/she just been saying this for so long that now he/she is not willing, or is ashamed, to admit that he/she is wrong!

In G-d's world of goodness and justice, when one comes to purify and be purified, he is assisted from Above. Despite the misguided way of the past, everyone has the capacity to change. People who open their eyes and realize their error, will at the end *voluntarily* accept the truth.

All civilized society accepts the said tendency as a perversion, and although in the past there were pagan tribes and "orders" which included these practices in their idolatrous rituals, history has shown that their memory is lost and their customs have vanished!

A special responsibility lies on the parents, educators

and counselors to educate those afflicted with this problem. Their duty is not to [educationally] "spare the rod," but at the same time to take a *loving* and *caring* attitude by extending a helping hand.

(From a Sichah of Purim, 5746)

CONFUSION OF GENDER IDENTITY

This is to acknowledge receipt of your letter of the 7th of *Av*.

There is surely no need to point out to you at length that one of the basics of our Torah, *Toras Chayim* [the Torah of life], is that Hashem is the Creator and Master of the Universe, whose benevolent Providence extends to each and everyone individually, and that He is the Essence of Goodness, and it is in the nature of the Good to do good, particularly in regard to our Jewish people, to whom he has given His Torah, *Toras Chayim*, of which it is stated that it is "our life and the length of our days," together with its *Mitzvos* whereby Jews live.

As you know, and indicate also in your letter, there are *Mitzvos* which apply to Jewish males, and those that apply to Jewish females, and the distinction in regard to the fulfillment of the *Mitzvos*, is a far-reaching one.

In light of the above, it is not clear why you should want to interfere with Hashem's blessings and contemplate a change of sex; especially as it would immediately bring in complications regarding Torah and *Mitzvos*, even assuming that there would be no problems in other areas. And since it would be quite plain and understandable, there is no need to elaborate on it.

As for your writing that you have sometimes had the

desire to have been born a female, etc. — it is not surprising that a human being cannot understand the ways of Hashem, Who surely knows what is best for every individual. However, if this desire is somewhat troublesome to you, it would be advisable that you should talk things over with a Torah-observant psychologist.

I suggest that you should have your *Tefillin* checked to make sure they are Kosher.

With blessing,

(From a letter of the Rebbe, dated 22nd of Av, 5745)

WHEN SEVERE MENTAL ILLNESS THREATENS A FAMILY

In reply to your late-arriving letter, in which you describe the situation in the family,[1] particularly with regard to health matters, etc., and you ask my opinion in this matter:

Generally speaking, your writing that the doctor stated that there is no hope for a full recovery is strange indeed, when in many known similar situations there was clearly a complete recovery.

I personally witnessed similar situations in which the individuals became better, and moreover, they have been fine for more than ten years; additionally, they married (for [one] of the individuals whom I have known the entire time was previously single; he has since married and has had children) and are engaged in established jobs.

---

1   The mother was suffering from quite a severe case of mental illness and there was a possible danger to the children.

With regard to a particular situation, it is impossible to know clearly and with certainty [about the eventual outcome], but clearly, the statement of the doctor that the situation is hopeless is definitely out of place. At the very most, he can say — and indeed all that a human being is capable of saying — that he does not take responsibility for the future [if his advice is heeded], but [he can say] no more than that.

With regard to the circumstances as you describe them, particularly that there are children who are still in their formative years, one must surely try to find any and all reasons and justifications for the marriage to remain intact.

Moreover — and this is of great importance — you should be in constant contact with specialists in this field, to rouse them and question them from time to time whether the new methods of treatment and new medications that appear quite often would be beneficial in this situation.

May the A-lmighty, Who oversees each and every individual with individual Divine providence, He Who is also "Healer of all flesh and Performer of wonders," direct you and all those mentioned in your letter in the path that is truly good for them, in a manner of overtly revealed goodness — goodness that is good both "to heaven and to man."[2]

May G-d will it that there be a rapid major improvement in the situation — particularly as we find ourselves now in the month of *Adar*, a month blessed with success for the Jewish people in all aspects....

(Igros Kodesh, Vol. XX, p. 183)

---

2   After *Kiddushin* 40a.

HOSPITALIZATION AND TREATMENT OF A MENTALLY ILL PATIENT

...Understandably, in such a situation, you are to follow the directive of the specialist about whom you write, [i.e., that your daughter be hospitalized,] for this will also benefit your daughter, *tichye* — surely she will be unable to receive all the benefits and care [at home] that she can receive in the surroundings suggested by the doctor.

However, before you [hospitalize her], you must find out more details about the particular institution; specifically, to establish a connection with the physician there, so that you will know what is transpiring with her, and most importantly — and this is easy to understand — that you be able to be certain that she is receiving the required attention and not treated in an indifferent manner.

May it be the will of G-d, "Healer of all flesh and Performer of wonders," that your actions on your daughter's behalf act as the conduit through which to receive G-d's blessings, as the verse states:[3] ["G-d will bless you] in all that you do."

It may be worthwhile — if you did not ascertain this until now — to acquaint the specialist with the state of her menses; if it is not in order, surely improvement in that area will assist in bringing about a general improvement in her overall status.

Inquire from him as well whether in these circumstances it would possibly make sense to medicate her with drugs from the class of aminocids and whether to treat her with shock therapy[4] and the like.

(Igros Kodesh, Vol. XX, p. 240)

---

3   *Devarim* 15:18.

4   At the time of the writing of this letter, shock therapy was far more commonly used than during present times, where it is used much more sparingly.

TEFILLIN AS A SPIRITUAL AID
IN HEALING SCHIZOPHRENIA[5]

[See to it that there is] scrupulous observance of putting on *tefillin* by those in need of a blessing [for healing], as well as by their fathers, etc.

The connection between [the healing effect of *tefillin* and the illness of schizophrenia] is very simple indeed, ([it is] in keeping with a manner of conduct that is also very simple [to comprehend]) — that of "measure for measure":[6]

Schizophrenia (whatever its cause) consists of a dissonance between actual facts (true reality) and how the ill individual "sees" them and comprehends them in his mind.

As a result, 1) his emotions are consonant with what he sees and perceives — panic and fear that others are seeking to harm him, etc.; 2) from time to time there are changes — from one extreme to the other: from unfounded fears to unfounded elation, etc., a total fragmentation of the psyche and perspective.

Tefillin [can be spiritually efficacious in combating the above, since] part[7] of the *mitzvah* [of *tefillin*] and its spiritual effect [consists of] submission of the heart (the emotions) and the brain (intellect) to the "G-d of truth,"[8] concerning Whom the verse states,[9] "I am G-d; I have not changed." The result: harmony between the mind, emotions and reality....

(*Likkutei Sichos*, Vol. XXXVI, p. 297)

---

5 Written in response to an individual who suffered from schizophrenia.

6 See *Sotah* 8b, 9b.

7 *Shulchan Aruch Admur HaZakein, Orach Chayim* 25:11.

8 *Yirmeyahu* 10:10.

9 *Malachi* 3:6.

ASSISTING SOMEONE
WHO IS A TOTAL RECLUSE

In reply to your letter from the 15th of *Tammuz* — that I just now received — in which you write about [the problems that] ... *sheyichye* [is having, and about the fact that he is a total recluse]:

It would seem from your letter that this individual should first and foremost actively begin seeking the company of others; this will serve as a good beginning for his overdue recovery.

Although — consonant with the saying of our Sages, of blessed memory, that "All beginnings are difficult" — his initial efforts to begin mingling with others will surely be difficult for him, he must force himself to do so. No doubt his friends will assist him in this matter.

Since, however, one should only demand of a person that which he is capable of doing, it is self-understood that my intent in the above is not that he suddenly change from one extreme to the other, i.e., that he interact with others for many hours a day. Rather, he should do this step by step, beginning with those with whom it will be easiest for him to connect.

He should do so, however, with the intent and goal that his interaction with others will continually increase to the point that he will do so naturally, not finding it a struggle to speak and mingle with others.

It would also be advisable for him to give a class to some group, doing so in the manner mentioned above: a relatively minor and easy subject that will not cause him overly great strain and require strenuous effort. In conjunction with the above — and this is of paramount importance:

He should be firm in his knowledge ([knowledge that is] based on the actual truth) that his present situation can improve one hundred percent — it need only be in a manner of [making these improvements] incrementally.

Additionally, his efforts should be based on the fundamental principle that service of G-d is to be with "joy and gladness of heart," as explained in the *Tur* and *Shulchan Aruch, Orach Chayim* ch. 231. And as stated above, it is more than likely that he will see for himself how eminently achievable this goal is.

Since you were the one who brought his question to me, you surely will not slacken your efforts; eventually the young man will be grateful to you for all you have endeavored to do for him, even if initially he will seem resentful.

(*Igros Kodesh*, Vol. XIX, p. 371)

DEALING WITH AGORAPHOBIA

A) Relate to your situation in an "easy" manner. In other words:

1) Be aware that truly many individuals suffer from the above, and yet live tranquil and serene lives, etc.

2) When you will need to enter a hall, a *shul* on *Yom Kippur,* and the like [do the following:] If it will be *easy* for you to do so, then do it. If not, do not engage in an internal struggle and battle; do not force yourself *at all* to do this. Pray at home (during the time of congregational prayer), and do not make an issue of this.

B) Enhance your religious observance. Your trust in G-d will then be strengthened as a matter of course, and this will lessen your worries, including the above worries (for *G-d* is watching over you).

(From a letter of the Rebbe, dated 3 Tishrei 5737)

INCREMENTAL PSYCHOLOGICAL PROGRESS

I received your letter of Friday, the 7th of *Iyar*, in which you ask my advice on how to assist Mr. ... [with his psychological problems]:

Generally speaking, it would be advisable to discuss the matter with a doctor; perhaps it is possible to find a doctor who had occasion to examine him.

I have also written a letter to him, which he may have shown you. It would be well to find an opportunity — of course without his knowing that I suggested this to you — to emphasize to him once again that the customary progress is measured in incremental steps and he should not expect to radically change himself in one fell swoop. Even if his progress is slow, in his circumstance, this incremental improvement is indicative of the manner of his progress.

(From a letter of the Rebbe, dated 17 Iyar, 5719)

KLEPTOMANIA

...With regard to your son ... *sheyichye,* who seems to display a propensity for stealing, G-d forbid:

You should turn to a professional, since this is a form of [psychological] weakness and doctors now have means of healing this ailment.

Understandably, this should not keep you from reciting an extra chapter of *Tehillim* daily as well as giving a few cents to *tzedakah* prior to *Shacharis* and *Minchah* specifically for your son's merit.

Inspect as well the *tzitzis* of your child's *tallis kattan* and make sure *he does not go with his head uncovered.* Check the *mezuzos* in your home as well.

If it is customary for the students to wear an additional head covering under the hat, he should be schooled in this as well. However, this should be done in an unostentatious manner, and [moreover,] it should emanate from the suggestion of his friends.

I hope that you will be able to convey glad tidings regarding the above.

(Igros Kodesh, Vol. V, p. 174)

LOBOTOMY

In reply to your letter of the 22nd of *Sivan* with the attached *pidyonos* in which you write about the idea of having surgery performed:

You do not, however, explain what form of surgery you are referring to — possibly you are referring to a lobotomy. If that is the case, then I do not — at least for the time being — agree with the idea of this operation, since until now this operation has very often proved unsuccessful.

It follows that all other forms of healing should be attempted before this step is taken, particularly since it is known that among the latest medications and therapies there are those whose positive results can only be discerned after a year or two.

It would be worthwhile for the doctor who is in charge of the patient's care to write in detail about the situation regarding the treatment of ... *tichye* until now in the manner that one doctor writes another. This will be shown to a specialist here....

(Igros Kodesh, Vol. XVII, p. 207)

In a follow-up letter to the woman's doctor, the Rebbe continues to explain his opposition to a lobotomy:

I acknowledge receipt of your letter from the 23rd of *Tammuz*, and I thank you for making the effort to describe the situation of the patient....

It is the opinion of the preeminent local specialists in this field, based on their experience in dealing with very many similar situations, that if the ailment has endured for many years and all other forms of treatment have been tried and have been unsuccessful, then they would be in favor of the surgery; [i.e., to perform a lobotomy].

Understandably, the final decision — as to whether the patient meets the above criteria — belongs to you, since the patient is under the care of the institution that you direct.

...With regard to the surgical procedure of lobotomy, a treatment that has been introduced in the last few years:

Like all scientific matters, particularly medical procedures, [and with lobotomies as well,] it is virtually impossible that there not be changes in doctors' attitudes and the extent of implementing procedures from year to year; the more extensive the reliable data of past outcomes, the more these changes are — based on past experience — well-founded and more enduring. Surely you are aware of all this much more than I.

In light of the above, it is readily understandable that any procedure that cannot be undone once performed, such as surgery, is to be utilized only after all other attempts have been exhausted — as you yourself write in your letter. Consequently, such a procedure is to be performed only when absolutely necessary and can in no way be further delayed.

This is why we witness that lobotomies in the United States are kept to a bare minimum, and even when performed they are only done after many years of [unsuccessfully] treating the ill patient with other forms of treatment. Even then, the majority of lobotomies are performed because — (as a result of a lack of funds) — the patient cannot be adequately [or] properly supervised.

Finally — and surely you know this better than I — even when the surgery is successful, here [in the United States], the instances where the patients are able to return to a normal life are extremely rare, if in fact they occur at all — notwithstanding the fact that you write "that almost all of them returned [after surgery] to a normal life."

As to the statement in your letter that you "do not desire to be a partner to murder": A lobotomy is not only an operation that involves excising a physical part of the body, it also involves excising part of the person's personality and psyche. As such, you can say that such a procedure also involves, as it were, a partial murder of the individual — it is merely that when there is no other option, one chooses this less extreme measure.

All the above explains my position regarding a lobotomy, an opinion that is based on the directive of our Torah, the "Torah of Life," that one should exercise any and all means even for the short-term salvaging of life.

This is particularly so with regard to mental illness, about which many matters are still unclear, both with regard to the causes of the illness as well as the manner of healing this illness. How much more so during the last few years, when critically important methods of treatment and fundamental changes are constantly occurring in the field of mental illness. It is therefore worthwhile to apply maximum effort to delay the lobotomy for as long as possible — until there is absolutely no other choice....

(Igros Kodesh, Vol. XVII, p. 282)

THE PSYCHIATRIST AS HEALER

...You invite my comments on the problems you mention in connection with your profession as a clinical psychiatrist in relation to your patients, specifically on moral and religious issues.

There is no need, of course, to point out to you that there can be no hard and fast rule that could be applied to all patients alike, since every individual is a world in himself. However, there are some points that would be valid in all cases.

To begin with, what is reprehensible from the view point of the Torah, called *Toras Chayim* (because it is the true guide in life), cannot be condoned.

This should not be confused with the principle of *pikuach nefesh* (a danger to life) which takes precedence over *Shabbos*, which is itself a directive of the Torah, requiring that the laws of *Shabbos* observance be temporarily suspended in such a case; it is not a violation of *Shabbos*, but a Divine directive like that of *Shabbos* observance which, in case of pikuach nefesh, is subordinated; and it is certainly not something left to human discretion or judgment.

Clearly, the said principle cannot serve as a basis for condoning other violations of Torah laws in order to help a patient get rid of guilt feelings, or make him feel better.

At the same time, there is also the instruction "The irate person is not a good teacher" (Ethics of the Fathers 2:6).

This applies, of course, not merely to a teacher who teaches any subject or theory, but also to one who teaches and guides and advises in matters of daily life and conduct.

A further helpful point to bear in mind is that through increased learning of Torah and stricter adherence to the mitzvot — though these are a must for their own sake — a Jew widens the channels to receive G-d's blessings, including deeper insights and understanding to cope with problems and to make the right judgments and decisions.

P.S. Needless to say, there is no point at all for you to change to another specialty in medicine that would not disturb your peace of mind, etc.

On the contrary, inasmuch as in your present profession you can now be guided also in your therapeutic methods by the Torah, it will be both a greater merit for you and of greater benefit to your patients — which makes it even more imperative that you continue specifically in your present field.

One of the ways to lessen and eliminate the personal emotional agitation, etc., is to consider your patients in the way the Torah explains their condition, namely, that "a person commits a transgression only because of a *ruach shtus* (an impulse of folly) that beclouds his mind"; in other words, because of mental illness. And the more serious is his malady when he does not want to recognize and admit that he is ill.

What has been said here is not to imply that it is necessary to tell the patient bluntly that what he has done is prohibited by the Torah and therefore he must not behave that way.

The approach should rather be in keeping with the method suggested by Maimonides when teaching a child. He writes that when teaching a child Torah, the child should be encouraged and induced to learn eagerly by promising and giving him candy and similar rewards that appeal to his childish mind, until such time as he will understand that the learning itself is the greatest reward.

Similarly, in the case of these patients whose knowledge

and standard are still on a child's level, for the essential thing is the actual result.

(From a letter of the Rebbe, dated Rosh Chodesh Adar II, 5736)

ADVICE TO A MENTAL THERAPIST

I acknowledge the receipt of your letter from the 27th of *Teves*, which I just received. You ask for a blessing and advice regarding [your efforts to psychologically heal]....

I will mention you in prayer and for a blessing at the holy resting place of my father-in-law, the Rebbe, that you succeed in your treatment of the above patient as well as all the other patients whom you assist.

With regard to your seeking advice: This is, after all, your profession, and "There are none so wise as those who have direct experience."[10]

It is particularly difficult to offer counsel from afar, as the conditions of the country, the family and so on, have a direct bearing on the situation. Those who observe the situation up close are always better able and more expert at arriving at a form of therapy.

However, since you have already written to me, and everything is by Divine providence, I wish to stress something that I have witnessed numerous times in similar situations:

In most similar situations, a decisive and effective method — which, to my amazement is not used, at least not as much as it should be used — is that of *hesach hadaas*, getting the patient to entirely remove his mind from thinking such [negative] thoughts.

---

10   *Akeidah, Parshas Noach,* Portal XIV.

The more the patient succeeds in ceasing to think about and to dwell upon those issues that are the cause of his problems, the greater will be the ability of the person's *natural* healing powers and his other positive and curative aspects to function with increased intensity and bring about healing.

Because of the special circumstances of those who are afflicted in this manner, one cannot always succeed when speaking to them openly and directly about the need to get rid of these thoughts.

However, the most important thing is that they actually stop thinking such thoughts; it really doesn't matter how to bring this about. This, therefore, can also be accomplished by having them become occupied with something that is totally unrelated to their state of health.

In order to bring this about in actuality, it is necessary to have them perform actions that lead to personal psychic gratification, such as by doing someone else a favor — something that in any case is acceptable to all [and therefore should not be difficult to convince them to do].

This is particularly so during our times, when instability is so great and people's needs are so numerous. It is relatively simple to find a way for these individuals to help other people — actions that are consonant with the [needs of the] locale and [of the] individual who requires healing.

An additional aspect to this manner of behavior is the fact that doing someone else a favor is not only good in itself, but carries with it its own reward — a truly great reward for a *mitzvah*.

[This reward is,] in the words of our Sages, of blessed memory:[11] "More than the householder does for the poor person [by

---

11   *Vayikra Rabbah* 34:10.

providing his needs], the poor person does for the householder [by providing him the opportunity to give *tzedakah*]."

There is more to say on this matter, but I am sure that for you, the above will suffice....

(Likkutei Sichos, Vol. XXXVI, p. 323)

TREATING BATTERED WOMEN AND CHILDREN

I received your letter of June 14th, in which you write about your communal activities, especially your involvement with a shelter for Jewish battered women and their children, and the difficulties connected with it.

I am confident that your awareness of the importance of the cause, and also seeing the help that it brings to these tragically affected women and children, makes it easier to overcome whatever difficulties you may encounter.

At the same time, it is well to bear in mind that the work you are doing demands a special sensitivity, [i.e.,] a sensitivity also from the viewpoint of *Yiddishkeit*, which, under the tragic circumstances, often is a factor to be reckoned with especially.

In light of the above, I trust that you will accept my suggestion that you should consult with at least one competent Rabbi who is familiar with the detailed and intricate factors involved in this activity, particularly insofar as *Yiddishkeit* is concerned.

In this connection, one must especially bear in mind that the requirements of the *Shulchan Aruch* [Code of Jewish Law] are fully adhered to so that everyone can benefit from the services, even if one is not a very strict observer otherwise.

For example, when a *glatt* kosher meal is served, everyone can enjoy it, whereas if it is not *glatt* kosher, it would present a problem to those who observe *glatt* kosher. It should also be remembered that when we are speaking about *Yiddishkeit*, it is something that deeply affects both the spiritual and physical aspects of Jewish life.

(From a letter of the Rebbe, dated 5 Tammuz, 5744)

HYPNOSIS AS A TECHNIQUE IN PSYCHOTHERAPY

...I would like to make a further point, though entirely not in my domain, namely, in reference to hypnosis as one of the techniques used in psychotherapy, as mentioned in your letter.

I have always been wary of any method that deprives a person of the free exercise of his will and which puts him in the power of another person, even temporarily — except, of course, in a case of a *pikuach nefesh* [a life-threatening situation].

Certainly I would not favor the use of such a method on a wider scale....

(From a letter of the Rebbe, dated 21 Adar II, 5738)

THE POWER OF FAITH AND GOOD DEEDS IN TREATING MENTAL ILLNESS

...I am making use of this opportunity to add another point, although this is [more] in your area, [i.e., psychiatry]:

The course of the illness and treatment of … proves (if proof is even necessary) how mighty the power of faith is in serving as a basis and foundation for man's inner peace and tranquility, and for minimizing — and at times even nullifying — inner personal conflicts as well as the "complaints" a person might have about those around him.

This is particularly so when this power of faith is related to, and finds expression in, actual deeds such as public service, performance of *mitzvos*, etc.

This is so, notwithstanding and in contrast to the school of thought that faith and religion demand of a person acceptance of a Divine yoke and suppression of one's instincts and natural inclinations, for which reason, [they maintain], it is not desirable in general, and particularly in the case of an individual who is in need of psychiatric treatment….

With esteem and blessings that you succeed in your career, healing the ill and leading them to a healthy life — life that is worthy of the term "life."

(From a letter of the Rebbe, dated 3 Tammuz, 5729)

MENTAL HEALTH DEPENDS ON SPIRITUAL HEALTH

From time to time I have the opportunity to see your writings on mental health in the newspapers.

For someone like you — particularly in light of the conversation I remember having with you in the past — it is superfluous to emphasize that healing the psyche of a Jew is dependent on his connection to Torah, concerning which it is stated,[12] "For they are our life and the length of our days" and the performance of its commandments, concerning which it is stated,[13] "You shall live by them."

If, with regard to all human beings, the health of the body is connected to the health of the soul, this is even more accentuated and apparent with regard to a Jew.

(Igros Kodesh, Vol. XXIV, p. 247)

LOGOTHERAPY

I find the articles of Dr. [Viktor] Frankel[14] ([of] Vienna) of particular interest with regard to the above [concept that a person's faith and its connection to good deeds and finding meaning in life enhance man's inner peace and tranquility, and minimize — and at times even nullify — internal and external conflicts].

However, to my surprise, it seems that his school of thought has not been sufficiently publicized and accepted.

Although there are many reasons why this may be so — among them that this is also related to the behavior offered by the attending psychiatrist, [i.e., the lifestyle lived by the psychiatrist himself] — the question remains [as to why his theories have not been sufficiently accepted].

(From a letter of the Rebbe, dated Tammuz 3, 5729)

---

12   *Maariv* prayer.

13   *Vayikra* 18:5.

14   Founder of Logotherapy.

POSITIVE AND NEGATIVE
FORMS OF PSYCHOTHERAPY

...Surely I need not make you aware of the directive of our Sages, of blessed memory, which states:[15] "A person should never give up hope," particularly as it is expressed in [the teachings of] *Chassidus*. The immediate conclusion to be drawn from this statement is that you should not cease your efforts in trying to influence the said individual to follow the proper path.

I believe I have already written to you regarding this matter, that we verily observe in similar circumstances that an indirect influence can have better results than trying to influence the individual directly.

I would also like to note the following in connection to your writing that the said individual finds himself under the care of a mental healer. It is not entirely clear to what kind of doctor you are referring. However, there is a specific class of therapists who commence their therapy by deriding G-d, spirituality, honoring one's parents, and the like.

If that is the type of therapist he is seeing, then even if the therapist is distinguished in his field, much examination and clarification is required in order to ascertain whether the benefit he may receive from him outweighs the long-time harm that may result [from this form of therapy] with the passage of time.

Of course, many such therapists have been effective and have healed utilizing virtuous methods, particularly since the time that one professor found the courage to declare and announce that (in opposition to the well-known individual who founded this form of therapy) belief in G-d and religious inclinations as a whole lead to a meaningful life, are of the

---

15   *Berachos* 10a.

most efficacious manners of healing, and so on and so forth.[16]

Nevertheless, for any number of reasons, this philosophy has not permeated many branches of therapy. It would therefore be worthwhile to find out more [about the therapist and his form of therapy].

(Igros Kodesh, Vol. XXII, p. 227)

SEE TO IT THAT THERAPY IS RECEIVED

...Enclosed is a copy of my response to ... Since that individual is unaware that I have sent you a copy, you on your part should try to find out in a diplomatic manner whether a psychiatric specialist was visited, what was said, and whether his instructions are being followed....

Certainly there are eminent specialists in this field in your locale, and it is worth making an effort that the advice of one of them is sought, as the matter about which was written about, unfortunately, is not all that uncommon in someone whose mental health is unstable.

There are many methods of healing this problem, particularly since — as stated in the letter — this matter began in conjunction with specific events, and knowing this makes it simpler to treat.

I await glad tidings from you with regard to all the above....

(Likkutei Sichos, Vol. XXXVI, p. 326)

---

16   See the previous letter under the title, "Logotherapy."

OLD AND NEWER METHODS OF TREATING MENTAL PROBLEMS

...You write that doctors are suggesting that you receive insulin treatments again. It is generally common to have this treatment repeated.

However, of late, many different methods have been discovered to treat such a type of illness, some of which say to continue with insulin and electroshock, etc. Lately, the method of treatment via medication and psychotherapy has become more prevalent.

May the "Healer of all flesh and Performer of wonders" speed your recovery through the method of treatment that is best for you.

...Understandably, regarding the course of action, you should follow the instructions of your doctor. However, you can make him aware (in a diplomatic manner) of the above.

(Igros Kodesh, Vol. XXI, p. 436)

...In reply to your question:

During the last few years, doctors here have vastly reduced the use of insulin and shock therapy and have replaced it with medications, and they are quite pleased with the results — although this form of healing takes longer to effect.

In any event, it is very important that — in a pleasant way — you see to it that he occupy himself with some form of labor or with some other matter that will not cause him to feel pressured.

(Igros Kodesh, Vol. XXII, p. 157)

MEDICATION RATHER THAN INJECTIONS FOR DEPRESSION

You write about taking injections, etc.:

I am surprised by this, since lately pills are used; they are both more effective and have less side effects. Moreover, there is no need to be in a hospital when they are used.

Here use is made of the [anti-depressant] Tofronil. Surely this medication or something similar to it is known about in *Eretz Yisrael*.

It is almost certain that a change of location, such as visiting friends for several days, will have a salutary effect, in a manner of overtly revealed good.

(Likkutei Sichos, Vol. XXXVI, p. 332)

"MIND-EXPANDING" DRUGS

I am in receipt of your letter of October 18th, which you write in the name of your friends and in your own behalf, and ask my opinion regarding the new drug called L.S.D., which is said to have the property of mental stimulation, etc.

Biochemistry is not my field, and I cannot express an opinion on the drug you mention, especially as it is still new.

However what I can say is that the claim that the said drug can stimulate mystical insight, etc., is not the proper way to attain mystical inspiration, even if it had such a property.

The Jewish way is to go from strength to strength, not by means of drugs and other artificial stimulants, which have a place only if they are necessary for the physical health, in accordance with the Mitzva to take care of one's health.

I hope that everyone will agree that before any drugs are taken one should first utilize all one's natural capacities, and when this is done truly and fully, I do not think there will be a need to look for artificial stimulants.

I trust that you and your group, in view of your Yeshiva background, have regular appointed times for the study of Torah, and the inner aspects of the Torah, namely the teachings of *Chassidus*....

(From a letter of the Rebbe, dated 20th of Marcheshvan, 5725)

chapter 6

OVERCOMING NEGATIVE TRAITS

CONTROLLING ANGER, ILL-TEMPER AND RAGE

KNOW THAT AFTER GETTING ANGRY AT SOMEONE YOU WILL HAVE TO BEG HIS FORGIVENESS

...With regard to your traits of anger and rage:

Ask your teachers to thoroughly explain to you the concept of individual Divine providence, which is a fundament of our faith.

The general substance of this concept is: The Creator and Conductor of the world oversees with individual providence each and every detail of your life, that is to say, you are constantly under G-d's supervision and He observes all your actions.

When you will ponder this matter many times until it is ingrained in your memory, this will surely diminish your temper and anger.

You should also perform that which the *Shulchan Aruch* commands, that when one offends another individual, even when done in a fit of anger, he is to beg his complete forgiveness.

It is difficult to ask forgiveness from another [after having caused them offense]. When you force yourself to overcome your [natural] reluctance [to ask forgiveness] and make sure to do so [as directed in the *Shulchan Aruch*], then every time you are about to become angry you will surely remember that afterwards you will have to ask that person's forgiveness.

This, too, will assist you in diminishing your character trait of anger and the like.

(Igros Kodesh, Vol. XVIII, p. 169)

BE EXCEEDINGLY COGNIZANT OF G-D'S PRESENCE

One piece of proven advice to control your anger is to contemplate how the entire world is filled with the glory of G-d, the King of kings, particularly as this [concept] is explained by the Alter Rebbe in chapter 41 of *Tanya* that, "Behold, G-d [Himself] stands over him and scrutinizes him and searches his reins and heart..., [i.e., his innermost thoughts and emotions, to see] if he is serving Him as is fitting."

When you remind yourself that you are in the presence of the blessed and exalted G-d, and at this very moment [of your anger] He searches your thoughts and emotions, etc., then there is no room for your anger.

(Igros Kodesh, Vol. XXIV, p. 124)

...You write about your trait of anger:

Engrave in your memory that which is stated at the beginning of chapter 41 of *Tanya* that, "Behold, G-d [Himself] *stands over him* ... and searches his reins and heart..., [i.e., his innermost thoughts and emotions]."

When you remind yourself of this, even while you are in the midst of your anger, that G-d is *literally* standing over you and searches your thoughts and emotions, etc., then your anger will surely pass.

(From a letter of the Rebbe, dated the First Day of Chanukah, 5730)

FOR ANGER AND DEPRESSION

To a woman suffering from depression and anger, the Rebbe responded:

Give several coins to *tzedakah* — *bli neder* — every weekday; study the [section entitled] *Shaar HaBitachon* in the book *Chovos HaLevavos*; check the *mezuzos* and their manner of placement.

(Likkutei Sichos, Vol. XXXVI, p. 298)

COMBATING ANGER THROUGH MEMORIZING PASSAGES OF TANYA

In reply to your letter of the 15th of *Sivan* in which you write that at times you suffer from the trait of anger:

Commit to memory the beginning of chapter 41 in the *Tanya* until page 112, line 2, [and conclude with the words]: "before the king." Also, ask your counselor (*madrich*) to explain to you the general content of *Iggeres HaKodesh*, Epistle 25. When you feel yourself beginning to get angry, repeat from memory the above [section of chapter 41] and the content of the above Epistle.

When you become used to doing so, your situation [vis-à-vis your trait of anger] will show continuous improvement.

(Igros Kodesh, Vol. XV, p. 270)

...In answer to the above person's question as to how he can rectify his temper — referring evidently to the trait of anger — it would be appropriate for him to study in depth the Alter Rebbe's *Iggeres HaKodesh*, Epistle 25, until he is well-versed in its contents. When he feels himself beginning to get angry, he should review in his mind the contents [of the Epistle].

(Igros Kodesh, Vol. XIV, p. 225)

COMBATING ANGER AND CURSING

In reply to your letter of the 21st of *Sivan* in which you write about the state of your health — you describe your ailment and that you were cured of it several times and after a period of time it returns:

It would be proper for you to question a specialist in this area and follow his instructions — and "permission was granted the healer to heal."

However, it is patently obvious that the fact that at times you use expressions that are the "opposite of blessings," this causes damage to your soul's health and thus also causes damage to your physical health [inasmuch as the health of body and soul are interdependent]. Moreover, the verse specifically states with regard to each and every Jew, "I shall bless those who bless you, ... [and curse those who curse you]."[1]

Taking into consideration that your occupation is that of a religious scribe, such conduct becomes even more unthinkable. Furthermore, that which is stated in *Kisvei HaAriZal* is known that at the time a person is angry, his soul

---

1   *Bereishis* 12:3.

is exchanged, G-d forbid — and surely it is not necessary to go on at length about a matter as plain and simple as this.

Moreover, since as the verse states, "As water reflects the face to the face, [so does the heart of man to man,"][2] when you act with forbearance, and only words of blessing and kindness will issue forth from your mouth, this is bound to evoke reciprocal feeling on the part of your wife, *tichye*, and peace and joy will reside in your home.

Also, study in appropriate depth *Iggeres HaKodesh*, Epistle 25 of the Alter Rebbe, the *Baal HaTanya veHaShulchan Aruch*, in which he explains the teaching of our Sages, of blessed memory:[3] "Whoever is in a rage resembles an idolater."

It would be appropriate for you to inspect your *tefillin*, especially the *tefillin* of the head, and after morning prayers to recite the daily portion of *Tehillim* as divided by the days of the month, *bli neder*.

(Igros Kodesh, Vol. XV, p. 237)

BECOMING UPSET AND ANGRY

You write about your nerves — that you frequently get very irritated and so on:

It would be advisable for you to read and also study the appropriate places where the matter of individual Divine providence is discussed according to the teachings of the Baal Shem Tov and the teachings of *Chassidus*. (Some of

---

2   *Mishlei* 27:20.

3   *Zohar* I, p. 27b; III p. 179a; *Rambam, Hilchos Deos* 2:3, quoting the "earliest sages;" *et al.*

these points are found in the Alter Rebbe's *Iggeres HaKodesh*, Epistle 25.)

Engrave these teachings in your memory by studying these teachings many times, so that you will easily remember the subject matter with all its details. This will also have an impact on your behavior, for understandably G-d's providence negates the concept of anger and even becoming upset (except for matters relating to the fear of G-d, as explained in *Iggeres HaKodesh*).

The above is eminently accomplishable and doable, for this matter [of not becoming upset or angry] is readily understandable on a rational level. Moreover, with just a bit of contemplation, one sees how this is a direct result of the simple belief that "there is no place devoid of Him.".…

(Igros Kodesh, Vol. XV, p. 240)

OVERCOMING ANGER AND HAUGHTINESS

…Regarding the traits of anger and haughtiness about which you write [and which you would like to master]:

Like all matters [that are to be accomplished], this matter too can only be accomplished in an incremental manner. The first step is not to give voice to the anger or haughtiness; by doing so you reduce the intensification of this trait — as we verily observe [that giving voice to an emotion heightens its intensity].

Concurrently, when either of these emotions become roused within you, you should meditate on that which is written in the beginning of chapter 41 of *Tanya* until [the end of the second line on] p. 56b. It would be proper for you to review this passage frequently, and better yet, that you commit it to memory.

In particular [it is important to refrain from anger] in light of that which is stated in the writings of the *AriZal* that anger causes one's soul to be exchanged. See also in the *sichah* of my father-in-law, the Rebbe, of blessed memory, of the 19th of *Kislev*, 5693, in which he explains the saying of our Sages: "Whoever is in a rage resembles an idolater."

(Igros Kodesh, Vol. XIV, p. 459)

NEGATIVE EFFECTS OF ANGER

I received your letter ... in which you write about your disputes with ... regarding the business.

...With regard to this trait [of anger], I must add the following:

We veritably observe that anger regarding worldly matters is not only not beneficial, but actually makes things worse.

This is particularly true with regard to interpersonal relationships, where when one person becomes angry it causes the other person to become angry as well and [at such times] the emotions overwhelm the intellect. Only later does the person realize that he shouldn't have said that which he said, [but by then it is too late to take back his words]....

(Igros Kodesh, Vol. VII, p. 36)

OTHER TRAITS

OVERCOMING LAZINESS

I am in receipt of your letter of the 4th of *Teves*, in which you write about the problem of laziness, etc., and you ask my advice as to how you can overcome it:

One of the effective ways of overcoming this difficulty is by deeply contemplating the notion that G-d is Omnipresent, at all times and in all places, as the Alter Rebbe explains in the beginning of chapter 41 of the *Tanya*:

"Behold, G-d [Himself] stands over him and scrutinizes him and searches his reins and heart..., [i.e., his innermost thoughts and emotions, to see] if he is serving Him as is fitting. Therefore he must serve in His presence with awe and fear like one standing before the King."

The point is to remember that inasmuch as G-d gives one the great gift of time and of mental capacity, etc., one must not waste these great gifts granted to him by G-d.

By way of illustration: Suppose a great and majestic king personally and graciously gave you a gift and he stands next to you in order to see what you will do with his gift; what would it look like if you would ignore his gift and go out for a walk or engage in some other pastime, etc.?

Surely it is unnecessary to emphasize to you this idea at greater length.

I will only add that the *yetzer hara* is never lazy, and is very busy and industrious in his efforts to distract a Jew from his service to G-d. Therefore, you must have a ready weapon with which to combat him.

For this reason, I suggest that you learn well and commit to memory the beginning of chapter 41 to which I referred above. Do so until these sacred words are engraved in your mind and consciousness, so that you will always be able to recall and ponder them whenever the need arises to overcome the temptation [to be lazy,] etc....

(From a letter of the Rebbe, dated 13 Teves, 5726)

SIBLING RIVALRY AND JEALOUSY

Blessing and Greeting:

I received your letter of October 18th, with the enclosure.

In reply, I want to say at once that the situation seems to me much better than your brother-in-law described it, for the reasons for your younger daughter's condition are not at all complicated.

The causes seem to lie in the fact that your daughter is subconsciously jealous of her older sister, and such a feeling manifests itself by a desire not to be interested in those activities where the person is unable to compete successfully. Therefore, your younger daughter shows little inclination to engage in the activities in which her sister is more successful than she.

However, since such is the attitude of jealousy, creating a subconscious feeling of guilt one is prone to compensate for it by an outward show at attachment. That is why she flies to defense of her sister if anyone should say anything disparaging against her.

All this confirms my general view of her conduct. I trust that her therapist fully agrees with this diagnosis, as he knows her better than I.

At the same time this diagnosis suggests also the method of therapy, namely, that every effort should be made to restore her confidence by offering her opportunities to engage in such activities where she can take a leading part and excel herself.

Needless to say this should be done in a gradual way, for, in her present state of mind she would be reluctant to undertake responsibilities all at once. But surely, both at school and in other cultural circles, there are opportunities for her to develop her artistic and other talents.

It would be psychologically beneficial to her if the activities would be of a kind in which her sister does not participate. The choice of such activities is fairly wide, and they could be cultural, charitable, or youth work among Jewish youth, and the like.

You do not mention anything about her physical health, especially in regard to puberty. It often happens that where these aspects can be regulated and normalized, there is an immediate improvement in the state of mind, for the emotional life is closely linked with the physical.

Finally, and this is just as essential, the physical and mental life of the Jew is directly linked also with the spiritual life.

I trust, therefore, that your daughter will take every effort to live up to the Jewish way of life in accordance with the Torah, which is called the Law of Life, and the *Mitzvos* whereby Jews live, since these are the channel and vessels to receive G-d's blessings. Needless to say, the parents themselves have to show a living example.

I would suggest that you have the *Mezuzos* of your home checked, to make sure that they are Kosher. No doubt you also know of the good custom of Jewish women to put aside a small coin for *Tzedakah* before lighting the candles.

Hoping to hear good news from you,

(From a letter of the Rebbe, dated 3rd of Cheshvan, 5721)

VANQUISHING SELF-PITY

As is understood from *Tanya* and many other sources, and as *verily* observed, self-pity is one of the most successful enticements of the evil inclination. [The person says to himself:] "Since G-d created me in this manner, since my situation is such, and since I am to be pitied more than any other human being — it is therefore impossible for me to do anything [constructive]; I am free of any and all obligations," and so on and so forth.

In order to forewarn someone approaching him and remonstrating, "How can this possibly be?!" [i.e., "How can you behave in this manner?!"] etc., etc., the person prefaces with the following:

"I am a good person and have no complaints against anyone; I [just] am incapable of doing anything. And even if you should say that I truly can act [constructively] but I do not desire to do so, this is my nature and what can I possibly do about it? I know all the complaints against my conduct, but [what can I possibly do, as] this is my nature?"

In light of the above [self-pity, the person unjustifiably] thinks to himself,] "Everything is *all right.*"

The underlying point [and principle in ridding oneself of all the above, is the saying of our Sages[4]], "If one says, 'I have toiled but not succeeded,' do not believe him," [for surely one will succeed if he truly applies himself].

The above applies to *all* matters in your life, in *all* their details.

(From a handwritten response of the Rebbe)

---

4   *Megillah* 6b.

chapter 7

MENTAL HEALTH OF CHILDREN, ADOLESCENTS AND TEENS

DEVELOPING A CHILD'S SELF-CONFIDENCE AND ESTEEM

Your letter of the 19th of *Kislev*, with enclosures, reached me just now.

Needless to say, to make an evaluation of a situation is very difficult, especially in a letter. However, this is not really necessary seeing that you have been in consultation with competent people, and you will no doubt continue to do so. Therefore, I can only make some general observations.

First of all, you surely know that nowadays such problems with children are very common, and in fact, probably in the overwhelming majority, although, of course not all problems are of the same degree, or in the same domain. I say this advisedly, for it seems from your writing that you are overly anxious, for which there is no real reason.

Usually, the final decision as to how to deal with children who have such problems lies with the administration of the school, after discussing the situation with the parents and being advised of the way the child is handled at home.

The reasons are understandable, since firstly, the administration are more objective than a parent can be. Secondly, they are also more experienced in such problems inasmuch as they deal with many children. And, after all, the parents can also express their opinion to help arrive at the best decision.

It is also well to bear in mind that a significant number

of such problems are usually straightened out in the course of time through the contact that the child has with other children and with the teacher and parents, because a child especially responds to the environment and to the persons with whom the child is in constant contact.

What surprises me is that there is a factor in the situation which is rarely, if ever, used. This is to give a problem child a role of leadership with a group of younger children, through some school activity and the like. This usually goes a long way to encourage the child's self-confidence, as well as making the child more sociable, etc.

I trust that this method could be used also in your situation — of course with the approval, and under the supervision, of the school administration.

The above will surely suffice for you and your husband to discuss the suggestions with the administration, to whom you may, of course, show this letter. I have strong confidence that the results in regard to each and all of your children will be gratifying...

(From a letter of the Rebbe, dated 5th of Teves, 5745)

RIDDING CHILDREN OF UNHEALTHY TRAITS AND HABITS

I received your letter, in which you ask my advice with regard to certain educational problems, especially how to influence the children to get rid of undesirable habits, etc.

Needless to say, these problems cannot be adequately discussed in a letter. However, experienced teachers and educators are usually their own best guides, for, as the saying goes, "None is wiser than the man of experience."

Besides, it is difficult to give advice from the distance, especially as the psychology of children may vary in certain aspects from one country to another.

Nevertheless, I would like to make one general point which can be universally applied in educational problems, a point which is emphasized in the teachings of *Chassidus*. I refer to the effort to make the children aware that they possess a soul which is a part of G-d, and that they are always in the presence of G-d (as explained in Chapters 2 and 41 of the *Tanya*).

When this is done persistently, and on a level which is suitable to the age group and background of the children, the children come to realize that they possess a great and holy quality which is directly linked with G-d, the Creator and Master of the world, and that it would therefore be quite unbecoming and unworthy of them to do anything which is not good.

At the same time they come to realize that they have the potential to overcome temptation or difficulty, and if they would only make a little effort on their part they would receive considerable assistance from On high to live up to the Torah and *Mitzvos*, which constitute the will and wisdom of G-d.

As for the problem of some children having a habit to take things not belonging to them, this may fall into one of two categories:

a. The attitude mentioned in the Mishnah in *Pirkei Avos* "Mine is thine and thine is mine." In this case the effort should be made to educate the child that just as it is necessary to be careful not to offend or shame another person, so it is necessary to be careful not to touch anything belonging to somebody else.

b. An unhealthy condition which should be treated medically by specialists who know how to handle such an aberration.

I would like to add one more point, which is also emphasized in the teachings of *Chassidus*, namely, to be careful that in admonishing children the teacher or parent should not evoke a sense of helplessness and despondency on the part of the child; in other words, the child should not get the impression that he is good-for-nothing and that all is lost, etc., and therefore he can continue to do as he wishes.

On the contrary, the child should always be encouraged in the feeling that he is capable of overcoming his difficulties and that it is only a matter of will and determination.

(From a letter of the Rebbe, dated In the Days of Chanukah, 5721)

WHEN A YOUNG PERSON REFUSES TO GO TO THE DOCTOR AND/OR FOLLOW HIS INSTRUCTIONS

This is to acknowledge your letter of January 3rd; in accordance with your request, I will mention your son in prayer.

Regarding the problem of getting your son to seek the advice of a doctor:

It is quite often the case that teenagers respond less to the influence of their parents than to the influence of their friends.

I believe that you will be able to find many suitable friends who will be able to speak to him [and convince him to seek a doctor's advice]. It would be better that your son not know that his friends were asked to convince him.

I wish to add that the unwillingness to seek the advice of a doctor or to follow his instructions is quite a common occurrence; and doctors generally know how to deal with such a situation.

One of the methods [to overcome the reluctance to take medication] is to prescribe a colorless and tasteless medicine that can be dissolved in milk and juice, so that [the young person] will not suspect [that he is taking a medication].

Since all blessings emanate from G-d, it is good to remember the following — a matter that at times people are inattentive to:

All members of the Jewish family are considered one entity and one body; that which is beneficial to one part [of this body] is beneficial to the whole.

Consequently, any and all additional efforts in increasing matters of goodness and holiness, Torah and *mitzvos* — particularly on the part of the parents — broaden the channels to receiving G-d's blessings for the entire family, and particularly to the individual who is in the most need of these blessings....

(From a letter of the Rebbe, dated 21 Teves, 5740)

STUTTERING AT AN EARLY AGE

...Stuttering at this [early] age is often the result of a sudden fright. When you ascertain what caused [his fright], it is much easier to rectify the situation, until the stutter will completely disappear. You should consult an expert in this field.

Surely I need not encourage you to enhance your study of Torah and performance of *mitzvos,* and that the more you do so the greater will be the improvement in all matters, particularly with regard to the above [problem of your son's stuttering].

(Igros Kodesh, Vol. XV, p. 313)

SUDDEN STUTTERING CAUSED BY SUDDEN FRIGHT

In reply to your letter of the 6th of *Tammuz,* in which you write about your youngest daughter ... *tichye,* who suddenly began to stutter:

You surely have requested the advice of a medical expert who specializes in this field, although in general you need not be overly alarmed, for most likely her stuttering is the result of a sudden fright. When you ascertain what caused her fright and explain to your daughter that her fear is groundless, her stuttering will gradually disappear.

It may be advisable to have your daughter sleep in a different bedroom, and also to have your *mezuzos* checked to make sure they are kosher. May G-d grant you success, so that you be able to convey to me the glad tidings that your daughter has fully recovered....

(Igros Kodesh, Vol. VI, p. 189)

ASSISTING ONE'S CHILD WHO IS SUFFERING FROM MENTAL PROBLEMS

1) Consult with the doctor with whom your daughter visits (or previously visited) of late. Although a doctor [who practices psychotherapy] will generally not divulge the condition of his patient to others, he will surely advise you as to how to deal with her. (From what I can gather from your letter, it would be worthwhile that you leave her to her own devices for a time.)

2) Understandably, it would be beneficial to find friends [of your daughter] who can influence her (without it being discernible that her parents asked them to intervene).

3) Enhancement of the parents' actions — that they be in even closer conformation to the *Shulchan Aruch*, i.e., to G-d's desires — increases G-d's blessings to the children as well....

(Likkutei Sichos, Vol. XXXVI, p. 324)

EXTRACTING A CHILD FROM HIS WORLD OF FANTASY[1]

...Since — as stated in the documentation (which is being returned under separate cover) — the child is interested in music and sings frequently, etc., you should try to use this to "reach" him, to attach him more firmly to his parents, *shey-ichyu*, etc.

{This should be accomplished by having his parents sing in his presence, telling the child that they will continue sing-

---

1   The above reply of the Rebbe was written concerning a child who was alarmingly withdrawing from reality into his private fantasy world.

ing if he fulfills a particular task, etc., or that they will obtain for him recordings of music that he favors, etc.}

Surely a child psychologist will be able to point out *numerous* methods as to how this can be accomplished.

(Likkutei Sichos, Vol. XXXVI, p. 325)

ASSISTING A YOUNG PERSON IN OVERCOMING HIS MENTAL PROBLEMS

You write about the young man [and his mental problems]:

You should seek the advice of medical specialists who focus on this area, for to our great misfortune the events that transpired with this young man have become all too common during the past few years.

Consequently, the doctors in this field already know how to deal with it, what medications to give, and also how one should conduct him or herself with such individuals after they return home.

One of the most important things is that he should not have spare time [with nothing to do], but should be occupied with matters that do not require intense concentration. It would also be beneficial for him to do some physical labor, at least part time.

This individual should also have his *bitachon* in G-d strengthened and should endeavor as much as possible to completely cease thinking about his past....

(Likkutei Sichos, Vol. XXXVI, p. 325)

DEALING WITH A HYPERACTIVE CHILD

In reply to a query as to how to handle a very "lively" and aggressive young boy, one who also had another medical problem, the Rebbe replied:

With regard to his "liveliness": Friends should be found for him who are as physically strong as he is. This will place at least some constraints upon him.

Regarding your second question about him: Ask the advice of a pediatric specialist, as this problem is not all that uncommon and it generally disappears with time, and appropriate medications speed the [healing] process.

(From a letter of the Rebbe, dated 11 Nissan, 5711)

BEDWETTING

...As is well known, doctors advise [that the child enjoy] tranquility and peace of mind to the greatest possible extent; to get the child to be unmindful of this situation [and surely not to exaggerate its severity]; diminished amount of liquids before going to sleep, and so on.

(Likkutei Sichos, Vol. XXXVI, p. 323)

ADOLESCENTS — SENSITIVITY TO THEIR NEEDS

...I would like to point out something you are undoubtedly aware of, and that is your son's age. He is in transition from youth to maturity, a time of life that entails considerable strain. During this sensitive period of adolescence, it is particularly important not to do anything that might aggravate the strain.

This is particularly true in a country such as this ... where even mature adults are prey to [forces of negative cultural and street] influence, and it requires much willpower not to succumb; how much more so where a teenager is concerned.

In light of the above, it is obviously the sacred duty of every near and dear one, and especially of parents, to do all things possible to promote the teenager's peace of mind and thereby make his struggles easier, and certainly to avoid anything which might weaken his willpower to resist the influences of the street, etc.

A further point: In the realm of faith, religion and feeling, every individual is a world unto himself. This is not the case in the realm of reason, where one can argue and convince and change the other person's mind. [In the former instances,] young people, especially, become attached to an ideal, particularly one that is expressed in actual behavior.

It can be extremely difficult to get such a person to change his feelings and conduct, and any effort to change his true nature, when applied to a young person during this sensitive period of adolescence, has serious implications.

(From a letter of the Rebbe in the year 5726)

TEENAGE YEARS AND FEELINGS OF BEING ALONE

...In reference to your stating that you have always been a loner and do not feel close to anybody, from which you seem to conclude that once again [in your present situation] you may have to make up your mind all by yourself:

As you realize — and this is also obvious from your letter —being a loner is not healthy, and this obviously has added to your confusion, as you mention in your letter.

If one does not feel a particular closeness to one's family, it is at least necessary to find social contact with people of one's own age and background, more or less, since such people must have gone through life and experienced the same general situations, allowing, of course, for individual exceptions.

...In conclusion, I would again like to volunteer an observation, though this time in a different vein, that you should not be so downhearted, since it is not unusual for young people of your age to feel a sense of confusion, or even frustration.

One needs only to feel for those who refuse to accept a helping hand from near and dear ones, including parents. I do not mean to say that one must readily submit to parental dictatorship, but neither does this mean that one should always reject parental advice and help in the hope that eventually things will straighten out themselves.

Of course, living in a nurturing, well-ordered, and disciplined atmosphere, willing to accept certain matters on authority without questioning everything from A to Z until one has been personally able to delve into all these matters — which is impossible — would go a long way toward improving the situation.

(From a letter of the Rebbe)

DEALING WITH ISSUES THAT CONFRONT AN ADOLESCENT MALE

Dr...

I am in receipt of your letter of May 13, in which you discuss the problem of m. You are quite right that it is a matter to be handled delicately but, surprisingly you do not mention that it is not to be treated by the same approach in all cases.

A further point to bear in mind is this. If, as you suggest, it should be explained to the person that it is "natural," or as some suggest that it should even be encouraged, then eventually all restraint will be removed, and the boy will indulge in it freely, with spiritual and physical consequences well known to you.

And judging by the majority of cases, such an approach would encourage overindulgence even from the "medical" point of view.

There is yet another consideration. When the person is told of the seriousness of the matter, there is at least the redeeming feature of having told him the truth.

Therefore, even if it may have a temporary undesired effect, one is at least certain in not having misled him, while when he is told that it is "natural" and he need not take it to heart, etc., it is not the truth, and he will sooner or later discover that he has been deceived or lulled, and the excuse that it was intended for his benefit may or may not satisfy him.

All this is without reference to the first and essential aspect of the situation, namely, the point of view of the Torah and Shulchan Aruch, which is most stringent about it, as the Rosh Yeshiva has no doubt explained to you.

From my knowledge of such cases, the majority of boys, and a majority by far, overcome this problem when they know its seriousness and are guided accordingly. This is why they do not come to the doctor's attention, while where restraint is removed it often becomes a medical problem,

I believe I mentioned in a previous letter that, knowing your family and background, I hope that in addition to the healing that you bring to your patients in their physical need you also help the spiritually, for in Jewish life the physical and spiritual are very intimately bound up together.

(From a letter of the Rebbe, dated 20th of Iyar, 5722)

REORIENTING OUR ASSESSMENT OF ADOLESCENT MALE ISSUES

A follow up to the previous letter:

Dr...

Thank you for your letter of Aug. 19th, which has just reached me, and in which you refer to the delicate matter which has been the subject of our recent correspondence.

With all due respect, I must disagree with your statement that there is a radical difference of attitude between the Jewish and medical-psychological points of view on this matter, in that the latter believe that there is no physical or psychological ill-effects.

I doubt very much whether physicians and psychologists do in fact generally hold this view. As far as i know most medical authorities do not share this view. Indeed, it is impossible that there should not be physical, and even more so psychological consequences, for every normal person is bound to experience "uneasiness", guilt *etc.* at doing something which is *not* natural.

What is even more painfully surprising, in my opinion, is the fact that physicians and psychologists who are concerned with finding a way to help the adolescents in this problem, are approaching this problem from the wrong end.

They should be the first to advocate early marriage, especially as there is already a marked tendency in this direction in the present day, except that, unfortunately, economic considerations prevent it from becoming more widespread.

Therefore, one would expect the medical profession to use its influence with local and state authorities to offer economic assistance to would-be early marriage candidates on the same principle that economic help is given to the aged.

To be sure, early marriage would not entirely solve the problem, since the age of puberty begins earlier, yet to prevent even a few years of this problem would be a very great achievement in the mental health of many people.

Therefore, instead of advocating an attitude as you describe, the M.D. and psychologists would be better advised to get to the *root* of the problem along the lines suggested above.

Needless to say, no single doctor can bring about a reorientation of view in the profession, and certainly the above observations are not intended as a personal reflection on you.

However, I venture to suggest that the reason why doctors have not come out in favor of early marriage with appropriate "fanfare" is the reluctance to advocate an "old-fashioned" idea! Yet, as already mentioned, there is an unmistakable tendency in this direction, and it is no longer considered so old-fashioned after all.

To return to the method of treatment, I see no reference in your letter to the point I made, which is "also" essential: As between the two methods, namely, to make light of it or to consider it reprehensible, the latter corresponds to the truth and natural order, while the other is at variance with same.

If the justification for the former is on the basis of selecting the lesser of two *evils*, then the truth should not be suppressed, at least. Thus, a certain disease may be and is treated by inducing malaria, on the principle of counteracting a greater evil by a lesser evil, but in that case no one will claim that malaria is no disease. Besides, this method is applied only where there is no other way.

As we are about to enter the month of *Elul*, when we will be saying twice daily "G-d is my light and my salvation" (Psalm 27), may G-d enlighten each and every one of us to utilize our capacities to the full in helping ourselves and others in every possible way...

If you will discuss the above with colleagues, I will be very interested to know their arguments.

(From a letter of the Rebbe, dated 28th of Menachem Av, 5722)

DEALING WITH AN OUT-OF-CONTROL YOUNG PERSON

In reply to your letter with the attached *pidyon nefesh* — which will be read at a propitious time at the holy resting

place of my father-in-law, the Rebbe, of blessed memory —
in which you write that you are at a total loss as to how you
should act with regard to your child:

There is the known, astute advice of our Sages, of blessed
memory, that there are three with whom one should conduct
himself with a "right hand that draws close — a child...."[2]

In your current situation, you should seek the advice of a
mental health doctor, since oftentimes — and possibly most
times — the conduct that you describe in your letter is a result of mental strain and the like. Quite often a doctor can be
quite successful in alleviating the matter.

In any event, in light of what you described to me, [it
seems that] banishing your son from the house can lead to
an even further deterioration of the situation and not be beneficial at all, as can readily be understood.

May G-d will it that you soon be able to convey glad tidings to me with regard to the above.

It is self-evident and patently obvious that the more you
and your family increase your observance of Torah and *mitzvos*, the more this will increase G-d's blessings in general and
the fulfillment of your specific requests in particular.

(Igros Kodesh, Vol. XV, p. 224)

MENTAL PROBLEMS OF A CHILD

I received your letter in which you write about the [men-
tal] problem of your daughter, Rivkah.

---

2   *Sotah* 47a; *Sanhedrin* 107b.

Judging by your description of her condition, it is somewhat surprising to me that she sees the doctor only once a month. However, I assume that you are in closer contact with him.

As for the question of making the trip to New York with your daughter to see me, I do not think it is advisable at this time, for it is impossible to foresee what effect this round trip might have on your daughter.

However, what I do consider advisable — and it is possible to arrange this without too much difficulty — is that your daughter have a change of environment for a couple of weeks. This would have a beneficial effect on her, inasmuch as she would not be in contact with the people in whose presence she feels so sensitive, etc.

Needless to say, every additional effort on the part of all the members of the family in matters of Torah and *mitzvos* would bring additional blessings to the whole family and particularly to your daughter, who is most in need of them.

(From a letter of the Rebbe, dated 12 Adar, 5718)

DEVELOPING A HEALTHY PERSONALITY — EARLY CHILDHOOD EDUCATION

True education is not merely the transmission of facts and imparting information.

The fundamental role of education, and one of its earliest and most important goals, is to mold a healthy, productive individual and to safeguard a person against his own potential negative tendencies and offensive traits. This is especially true of early childhood education.

On his own, a person is not objective in evaluating his own characteristics. A person's inclination and his own innate, materialistic nature and self-love will often "bribe" an individual into a distorted view of his negative traits.

Proper education is therefore required to help an individual cultivate and carefully focus his or her introspective inquiry.

The earliest narrative related in Scripture tells the story of the "Tree of Knowledge," which was "desirable to the eyes" and, therefore, was also assumed to be "good to eat" (*Bereishis* 3:6).

As a result of the overpowering temptation, G-d's warning was disregarded and death came to mankind. In other words, tempting pleasures can often "blind" one's better judgment.

Solomon, the wisest of men, taught us:

"He who spares the rod hates his son: but he who loves him, chastises him early." (*Mishlei* 13:23)

This means that effective education and childhood training must incorporate a strong approach to form the positive personality of the individual, and to rid the child of "unsavory" dispositions.

Laxity in this area would represent *hatred* for our children, and experience has shown that those children who were not properly and strictly brought up, but were raised with a liberal, "free" upbringing, came back to their parents later with serious complaints.

Eventually they blame their "rod-sparing" parents and teachers for their personal behavior and their unmodified, negative inclinations and traits.

In our era we know this *a posteriori,* i.e., deducted from our own experience.

This fundamental role of education is not only pertinent in modifying the *acquired* characteristics and habits that a child picks up by *"nurture,"* but also in relation to the inborn predispositions which come to the child by his *"nature."*

Here, too, the child must be educated, and his natural conduct must be modified with a strong and positive involvement on the part of the parents and of the educator.

For if they "spare the rod," waiting for the child to mature on his own and *independently* learn to overcome his inclinations, in the interim the child will cause harm to himself and sometimes also to his surroundings. The firm education "rod" is the best *favor* for the child.

(Purim, 5746)

chapter 8

ASSISTING THE MENTALLY CHALLENGED AND IMPAIRED

ON JUDAISM AND PEOPLE WITH DISABILITIES

The following is a correspondence of the Rebbe, and Dr. Robert Wilkes, at the time director of the Child Development Center at the Coney Island Hospital, on the subject of assisting people with special needs.

In the initial stages of the correspondence, the term "retarded" is often used. However, in a letter to participants in a conference on the "Issues and Needs of Jewish Retarded," (brought below), the Rebbe expressed his view that this was an improper characterization, and that he much preferred the term "special."

FIRST LETTER FROM DR. ROBERT WILKES TO THE REBBE

Coney Island Hospital

2601 Ocean Parkway • Brooklyn, New York 11235 • 212-743-4100
Child Development Center

August 9, 1979

Rabbi Menachem Mendel Schneerson
Lubovitcher Rebbe
770 Eastern Parkway
Brooklyn, N.Y. 11213

Dear Rabbi Schneerson:

As a Jewish social worker and the chairman of Region II Council For Mental Retardation in Brooklyn, I would be most interested in learning what your views are regarding "the care and education of Jewish retarded individuals"—those persons who, from birth, are slow in thinking, speaking and learning.

For many years, the retarded individual, especially the severely retarded, was placed in a large, state-operated institution, often quite a distance from the individual's home and community. During the past few years, efforts have been made to create "group homes" in all our neighborhoods throughout the city so that parents who cannot continue to care for their retarded sons or daughters have the choice of placing their child in a small, home-like setting: situated either within or nearby the individual's community.

This policy of creating "group homes" for the retarded—Jewish as well as non-Jewish—has been a source of controversy and often bitter opposition pitting parent against parent, neighbor against neighbor, and political leaders against one another. The basis for these heated discussions include predictions about lowering the economic value of homes in a community; fear that retarded individuals will commit vandalism or, even worse, commit crimes; and that the retarded themselves will feel uncomfortable surrounded by normal people. On the other hand, parents of the retarded want their children to live in a safe and healthy environment.

How may we view this issue—that is, caring for individuals who have a disability which requires life-long care and supervision—from a Jewish perspective? As a concerned Jew, I care very much about our Jewish community: how we treat one another and how we conduct ourselves as human beings. I am particularly interested in your comments and opinions, because the Lubavitcher movement, with its deep concern for every Jewish individual's welfare, has added a spiritual dimension—a spark—to all our lives!

As a married man with—thank G-d—two beautiful, healthy children (ages 2 and 5), I am also aware that there has to be an equal concern for both the individual as well as for one's total community. The question is: how do we protect and safeguard all of our Jewish children—the retarded and the non-retarded—so that they can have the opportunity to grow, to develop, and to live "Jewishly"?

I would also welcome the opportunity to discuss any of the above with you or your representatives. Thank you for your cooperation.

Respectfully yours,
Robert Wilkes,
Assistant Program Director/
Chairman, Region 11 Council For Mental Retardation

FIRST LETTER FROM
THE REBBE TO DR. ROBERT WILKES

JEWISH EDUCATION FOR KIDS
WITH SPECIAL NEEDS

By the Grace of G-d
22 *Av*, 5739
[August 15, 1979]
Brooklyn, N.Y.

Mr. R. Wilkes, Asst. Program Director/
Chairman, Region 11 Council For Mental Retardation
Coney Island Hospital
2601 Ocean Parkway, Brooklyn, N.Y. 11235

Greeting and Blessing:

This is in reply to your letter of Aug. 9, in which you ask for my views on "the care and education of Jewish retarded children," outlining some of the problems connected therewith and prevailing policies, etc.

I must, first of all, make one essential observation, namely, that while the above heading places all the retarded in one group, it would be a gross fallacy to come up with any rules to be applied to all of them as a group. For if any child requires an individual evaluation and approach in order to achieve the utmost in his, or her, development, how much more so in the case of the handicapped.

Since the above is so obvious, I assume that you have in mind the most general guidelines, with a wide range of flexibility allowing for the necessary individual approach in each case. All the more so, since, sad to say, our present society is poorly equipped in terms of manpower and financial resources to afford an adequate personal approach to each handicapped boy and girl. Even more regrettable is the fact that little attention (at any rate little in relation to the importance of the problem) is given to this situation, and consequently little is done to mobilize more adequate resources to deal with the problem.

Now, with regard to general guidelines, I would suggest the following:

(1) The social worker, or teacher, and anyone dealing with retarded individuals should start from the basic premise that the retardation is in each case only a temporary handicap, and that in due course it could *certainly* be improved, and even improved substantially. This approach should be taken regardless of the pronouncements or prognosis of specialists in the field. The reason for this approach is, first of all, that it is a *pre*condition for greater success in dealing with the retarded. Besides, considering the enormous strides that have been made in medical science, human knowledge, methodology, and know-how, there is *no* doubt that in this area, too, there will be far-reaching developments. Thus, the very confidence that such progress is in the realm of possibility will inspire greater enthusiasm in this work, and hopefully will also stimulate more intensive research.

(2) Just as the said approach is important from the viewpoint of and for the worker and educator, so it is important that the trainees themselves should be encouraged both by word and the manner of their training to feel confident that they are not, G-d forbid, "cases," much less unfortunate or hopeless cases, but that their difficulty is considered, as above, only temporary, and that with a concerted effort of instructor and trainee the desired improvement could be speeded and enhanced.

(3) Needless to say, care should be taken not to exaggerate expectations through far-fetched promises, for false hopes inevitably result in deep disenchantment, loss of credibility and other undesirable effects. However, a way can surely be found to avoid raising false hopes, yet giving guarded encouragement.

(4) As part of the above approach, which as far as I know has not been used before, is to involve (some of) the trainees in some form of leadership, such as captains of teams, group leaders, and the like, without arousing the jealousy of the others. The latter could be avoided by making such selections on the basis of seniority, special achievement, exemplary conduct, etc.

(5) With regard to the efforts which have been made in recent years to create "group homes" for retarded individuals, which, as you say, has been a source of controversy, it is to be expected that, as in most things in our imperfect world, there are pros and cons. However, I believe that the approach should be the same as in the case of all pupils or students who spend part of their time in group environments: school, dormitory, summer camp, etc., and part of their time in the midst of their families, whether every day, or at weekends, etc. Only by individual approach and evaluation can it be determined which individual fits into which category.

(6) There is surely no need to emphasize at length that, as in all cases involving Jews, their specific Jewish needs must be taken into account. This is particularly true in the case of retarded Jewish children, yet all too often disregarded. There is unfortunately a prevalent misconception that since you are dealing with retarded children, having more limited capabilities, they should not be "burdened" with Jewish education on top of their general education, so as not to overtax them. In my opinion this is a fallacious and *detrimental* attitude, especially in light of what has been said above about the need to avoid impressing the child with his handicap. Be it remembered that a child coming from a Jewish home probably has brothers and sisters, or cousins and friends, who receive a Jewish education and are exposed

to Jewish observances. Even in the American society, where observant Jews are not yet in the majority, there is always some measure of Jewish experience, or Jewish angle, in the child's background. Now therefore, if the retarded child sees or feels that he has been singled out and removed from that experience, or when he will eventually find out that he is Jewish, yet deprived of his Jewish identity and heritage, it is very likely to cause irreparable damage to him.

On the other hand, if the child is involved in Jewish education and activities, and not in some general and peripheral way, but in a regular and *tangible* way, such as in the actual performance of *Mitzvos*, customs and traditions, it would give him a sense of belonging and attachment, and a firm anchorage to hold on to, whether consciously or subconsciously. Eventually even a subconscious feeling of inner security would pass into the conscious state, especially if the teacher will endeavor to cultivate and fortify this feeling.

I am, of course, aware of the arguments that may be put forth in regard to this idea, namely, that it would require additional funding, qualified personnel, etc., not readily available at present. To be sure, these are arguments that have a basis in fact as things now stand. However, the real problem is not so much the lack of resources as the prevailing attitude that considers the Jewish angle as of secondary importance, or less; consequently the effort to remedy the situation is commensurate, resulting in a self-fulfilling prophecy. The truth of the matter is that if the importance of it would be seen in its true light that it is an essential factor in the development of the retarded Jewish child, in addition to our elementary obligation to all Jewish children without exception, the results would be quite different.

Perhaps all the aforesaid is not what you had in mind in soliciting my views on "group homes." Nevertheless, I was impelled to dwell on the subject at some length, not only because it had to be said, but also because it may serve as a basis for solving the controversy surrounding the creation of "group homes" for those children who are presently placed in an environment often quite distant from the individual's home and community, to paraphrase your statement.

Finally a concluding remark relating to your laudatory reference to the Lubavitch movement, "with its deep concern for *every* Jewish individual's welfare," etc.

Needless to say, such appreciation is very gratifying, but I must confess and emphasize that this is not an original Lubavitch idea, for it is basic to Torah Judaism. Thus, our Sages of old declared that *ve'ohavto lere'acho ko'mocho* ("Love your fellow as yourself") is the Great Principle of our Torah, with the accent on "as yourself," since every person surely has a very special, personal approach to himself. To the credit of the Lubavitch emissaries it may be said, however, that they are doing all they can to implement and live by this Golden Rule of the Torah, and doing it untiringly and enthusiastically.

May the *Zechus Horabbim*, the merit of the many who benefit from your sincere efforts to help them in their need, especially in your capacity as Regional Chairman of the Council For Mental Retardation, stand you in good stead to succeed in the fullest measure and stimulate your dedication for even greater achievements.

With esteem and blessing,

[sig.]

SECOND LETTER FROM DR. ROBERT WILKES TO THE REBBE

There was a second letter from Dr. Robert Wilkes to the Rebbe dated September 19, 1979 as referenced in this letter from the Rebbe to Dr. Wilkes.
At the time of publication, this letter was missing and was therefore not available for publication.

SECOND LETTER FROM THE REBBE TO DR. ROBERT WILKES

SPECIAL CHILDREN AND SHABBAT

By the Grace of G-d
13 *Tishrei*, 5740
Brooklyn, N. Y.

Dr. R. Wilkes, DSW
Chairman, Region-II Council for Mental Retardation
Coney Island Hospital
Brooklyn, N. Y.

Greeting and Blessing:

Because of the intervening High Holidays, my acknowledgment of your letter of Sept. 19th has been somewhat delayed.

Of course you have my permission to disseminate my letter, if it can serve a purpose in promoting the cause of education in general, and of the "special children" in particular. Indeed, since every child is special and deserves special attention, how much more so those who are "slower" than others.

However, if the letter is to be disseminated, an important reservation must be added, which though self evident to a person like yourself, may not be self evident to others, and therefore must be clearly stated to them. hence was not mentioned ·in my letter to you.

It is that in all that has been said in regard to Jewish children - it is first necessary the requirement of the Halacha in regards to these children - depending on their age and 'their level of' comprehension to make sure that the facilities meet these requirements in terms of Kashrus, *Shabbos, Tefillin.* etc.

To add a timely note appropos of the New Year, which is a "Seventh Year, a Year of Shemittah" (Sabbatical Year), and also began on the day of the holy Sabbath, the main characteristic of the Sabbath day is that it is a day of "delight" (Oneg) for young and old, as it is written, "You shall call the Sabbath a delight," which, by extension, also characterizes the entire New Year.

Hence, if there are children and adults who, for whatever reason, are in a situation which precludes them from enjoying the "Sabbath" delight, it behooves anyone who becomes aware of this to do everything possible to enable them to participate in this delightful experience. The fact that the knowledge of the existing situation has reached certain organizations and individuals - and everything is by Divine Providence, is a further indication that they are in a position to act on this knowledge. Should there be any difficulties, even real ones and not exaggerated or imagined, it only means that they have commensurate capacities to overcome them, For as with all Divine commandments, the obligation is given together with the capacity to carry it out,

Thus, in the final analysis, it is largely a matter of persona, will and determination. With esteem and blessing of Chag Someiach,

P.S. I take the liberty of enclosing a copy of my New Year

message, in which the significance of the New Year, 5740 as a "Year of Sabbath" is more fully discussed.

P.P.S. I note in the zerox copy of my letter, which you enclosed with yours, that the word "yet" - added by hand (P, 2, 8 line from bottom), as well as the line underscoring the word "tangible" (Beg . P. 3) does not appear clear, No doubt this will be rectified in the other copies.

THIRD LETTER FROM
THE REBBE TO DR. ROBERT WILKES

REQUEST FOR UPDATE

By the Grace of G-d
2nd of *Shevat*, 5740
Brooklyn, N.Y.

Dr. R. Wilkens, DSW
Chairman, Region II Council for Mental Retardation
Coney Island Hospital
2601 Ocean Pkway.
Brooklyn, N.Y. 11235

Greetings and Blessings

Since our exchange of correspondence some months ago, I have not heard from you.

I am interested to know if there have been any developments in regard to the subject matter of our correspondence, and, if so, would appreciate your letting me know about it.

With all good wishes, and
With blessing,

THIRD LETTER FROM DR. ROBERT WILKES TO THE REBBE

February 19, 1980

Rabbi Menachem M. Schneerson
770 Eastern Parkway N.Y. 11213

Dear Rabbi Schneerson:

In a rather short period of time (since we last exchanged letters) there have been a number of exciting developments such as additional services being created for the Jewish retarded individual but-at the same time - some new developments which may in the long run prove detrimental to our objective of giving "special" care to the needs of the Jewish retardate and his/her family. Before I list and explain some of these exciting and positive developments as well as some of the more ominous concerns, I want to let you know that I did make the effort to write you again but my letter probably never reached you (attached is a copy of my letter dated 9/19/79). Although I have shown your statement to many different people (Jewish as well as non-Jewish), I have not sent it to any publications because I wanted to first get your written authorization.

A few weeks ago I received a call from a columnist from the Jewish Press - who I believe writes a weekly column called "Challenge" - who wanted to publish your letter (I forgot to ask him how he got hold of it). I informed him that, since I hadn't received your permission, he should first get in touch with you. Let me say this: by your letter appearing in the Jewish Press, which has a rather larger readership, it would give many families with handicapped children a tremendous feeling of comfort and support. And families with retarded children need all the support they can get just to "keep going" from day to day!

What are some of the exciting new developments? Federation of Jewish Philanthropies has decided to expand, on a full-time basis, their religious/cultural program started by a young, dynamic, and very competent orthodox Rabbi (Martin Schloss). Rabbi Schloss and his dedicated staff assist Jewish men and women, many of whom are severely retarded, in Jewish living - e.g. celebrating Chanukah by lighting the menorah, singing Chanukah songs, learning how to cook special holiday dishes. To Rabbi Schloss' credit he includes in his activities not only the retarded individual but their families. His program was only a few weeks in existence when it spread like wild fire throughout the city that 'finally' there is a Rabbi who loves the retarded and who wants to give them an opportunity to experience Yiddishkeit.

At about the same time Rabbi Schloss was demonstrating the need for a religious program, three Jewish orthodox mothers of retarded children (Mrs. R. Feinerman, Mrs. P, Gaffney, Mrs. T. Stone) began to organize other orthodox mothers with retarded children. The response to their request for a meeting was overwhelming. They received hundreds of phone calls from Jewish mothers throughout the city and even from other states: all of whom had one thing in common: the desire to see our Jewish community to do more for its developmentally handicapped children (retarded, epileptic, cerebral palsy, brain injured, autistic). They have had two or three meetings. I have sent them some material including your letter. What these mothers find most frustrating and anguishing is that they would like to see their children in a "Yeshiva" learning Chanukah songs rather than Christmas carols. Even more heartbreaking is the fact that some prominent orthodox Rabbis have publicly made extremely insensitive remarks about the retarded.

Another positive development is that Federation of Jewish Philanthropies (I have had meetings with Rabbi I. Trainin and Rabbi S. Sharfman) will soon distribute a new brochure that lists all of its services for the Jewish retarded individual and his family. For some time many Jewish families were under the impression that Federation had nothing to offer their developmentally handicapped children. In addition, Rabbis Sharfman and Trainin expressed interest in sponsoring a major conference on the Jewish retarded child so that perhaps for the first time we can publicly acknowledge that our Jewish community has retarded children who need all of our help.

What are some of the more ominous developments? Throughout the city there will be an increasing push to create small community group homes for the retarded. There is a legal document referred to as the "Willowbrook Consent Decree" which stipulates that by 1981 a certain number (in the thousands) of retarded individuals must be living in these community residences throughout New York City. It is a good decree because it will give many retarded people a chance to live, hopefully, like a human being.

In Brooklyn, where there are already about 35-40 group homes in operation, 47 more such residences (under the sponsorship of private, voluntary agencies) will be opening within a year. About 20 additional homes will be sponsored by the state — in all likelihood, the state will care for nonambulatory, multihandicapped individual. From what I have recently learned, neighborhoods such a.s Coney Island, Brighton Beach, Sheepshead Bay which have either none or very few community residences for the retarded will begin to feel rather heavy pressure to open community homes (usually from 8 - 10 residents per/ home) in their respective areas.

What is ominous is the fact that whereas previously Jewish agencies could recruit Jewish clients, the pressure to create more and more community residences within a fixed time period has allowed state officials to "pre-select" which clients are to be chosen for any given residence. In other words, private, voluntary agencies are finding that, if they want to obtain funds to operate a community residence for the retarded, they must "accept" the clients chosen by the state authorities. I have attempted without success to call Sanford Solender, Executive Vice-President of Federation of Jewish Philanthropies, to alert him to this new development so that he can use whatever political connections he has available to him to express his Jewish agencies not be prevented from serving primarily Jewish retarded individuals. Only Jewish agencies have Kosher Kitchens in their community residences.

There are so many things I want to write about - I am afraid of turning this letter into a lengthy essay. Another development which is ominous but regretfully not new is the fact that many Hebrew Day Schools "test" children with I.Q. tests to determine if this or that child has the intellectual ability to be enrolled in their school. If the answer is "no", then the parents have to "shop" around for another Yeshiva - which may also have a policy of testing children prior to enrollment. Although I am not against psychological tests if and only if they are utilized to help a teacher or a parent on how to best approach a particular child who may be experiencing difficulty in a subject, I find it almost impossible to believe that our Jewish community has adopted this practice of selecting "who" will be exposed to Torah and who will not. Perhaps the best word I can find to describe my feelings about this practice is "appalled." To my dismay, this practice is widespread and not easily changed. But I am determined to do what I can to change it no matter how long it takes.

Let me conclude this letter by informing you that in the weeks ahead a number of people such as Rabbi Schloss, orthodox Jewish mothers, and other concerned individuals are planning to get together to begin to coordinate our efforts so that whatever we do will have the maximum impact. I have been very fortunate to have two very good friends (who also happen to be my colleagues at Coney Hospital), Dr. {Rabbi) Benjamin Sharfman and his son-in-law Dr. (Rabbi) Gerald Schwartz, both psychologists, who have inspired me to "move the Jewish community always another step higher on the rungs of charity.

Your correspondence has been for me a great source of pride and honor which has given me a greater sense of hope that one day all Jews will treat each other with respect and compassion. Please feel free to call me should you need additional information. If you would like to discuss anything in this letter in more detail, I would be available to meet with you or your representatives. Let me take this opportunity to wish you and your family a very happy and healthy Purim.

Respectfully yours,
Robert Wilkes,
DSW Chairman,
Region II Council For Mental Retardation

LETTER FROM DR. WILKES TO RABBI BUTMAN

Region II Council For Mental Retardation
April 3, 1980

Rabbi Shmuel M. Butman
Jewish Press
338 - 3rd Avenue
Brooklyn, N.Y. 11215

Dear Rabbi Butman:

The reason I've waited this long to send you the enclosed material including the exchange of letters between Rabbi Menachem Mendel

Schneerson and myself is twofold: (a) only recently received Rabbi Schneerson's letter - dated 13 Tishrei - which gives me permission to disseminate his correspondence; and, (b). just received the minutes from Rabbi Isaac N. Trainin (Federation of Jewish Philanthropies) which documents Federation's decision to sponsor a major conference vis vis the needs of the Jewish retarded and his/her family in October/ November 1980.

In some of the letters that I wrote I have underlined these sentences which reflect the essence of my thinking - my way of letting you know what I would like you to emphasize. On the other hand, where I prefer you not to quote me I have put sentences in brackets.

Since Rabbi Schneerson's letter (dated 22 Av, 5739) is, to my knowledge, the only "statement" issued on the subject of retardation by an "outstanding Torah authority," I would hope that the Jewish Press would give his words prominence the week your column gets published. Perhaps that week the Jewish Press can have an editorial which challenges the practice of testing preschool children for enrollment in Hebrew Day Schools. The paper can also list services (with telephone numbers and names of contact persons)available to families of retarded and developmentally disabled individuals.

In other words, I think our Jewish community has to recognize yes - we want and need Jewish scholars - but, in the final analyses, what counts is that our people care about each other, respect each other, and appreciate each other's contribution irrespective of one's 'intelligence quotient.

This is one issue - the love and care of Jewish handicapped - that can bring all Jews together. I felt very reassured when Rabbi Schneerson in one of his letters explained that with every Divine obligation (mitzvah) there is the capacity to fulfill that obligation. There is no question that we will need not only "funds" but the energy and the will to modify our opinions, to think about issues which we may prefer not to deal with, and to tolerate honest differences of opinion.

I am convinced that if our Jewish community can provide for the education and the well-being of all of our children, we will merit the coming of the Moshiach. Thank you for your cooperation.

Sincerely yours,

Robert Wilkes, DSW
Chairman, Region I I
Council for Mental Retardation

"'I could not think of any other phrase which could adequately describe or characterize the Lubuvitche Rebbe. Although I am not an orthodox Jew, I still feel a close and warm attachment to Rabbi Schneerson. Perhaps it is his deep and abiding caring for all Jews that has given me (and I'm sure to many others!) the inspiration and vigor to do what I'm doing.

RW/ma

FOURTH LETTER FROM DR. ROBERT WILKES TO THE REBBE

August 12,1980

Rabbi Menachem M. Schneerson Lubavitch
770 Eastern Parkway,
Brooklyn, New York 11213

Dear Rabbi Schneerson:

Rabbi Dr. Benjamin Sharfman, chairman of Federation's prospective conference on issues and needs of the Jewish retarded, has given me the honor and privilege to invite you (and/or your representatives) to address this conference. [...]

What should be remarkable about this conference is that not only will the participants be discussing how to make all aspects of Jewish living (e.g., education, community living, recreation, worship) available to the developmentally disabled individual and his/her family but also the participants, perhaps for the first time for a "Jewish" conference. [...]

It is no secret that the Lubavitch movement—perhaps more than any other Jewish group—has emphasized the critical significance of Jewish education for all Jewish boys and girls as well as the overall need of Yiddishkeit for all Jews. We would welcome a statement from you prepared for this occasion: to be read at the conference by either yourself or by a representative. You may also consider the possibility of sending a specially prepared taped message. Please feel free to consider any form of communication which you think would be most meaningful. [...]

May I take this opportunity to once again thank you for your continued interest and support. [...]

Wishing you and your entire family a very happy and healthy New Year.

> Respectfully yours,
> Robert Wilkes, DSW
> Chairman, Brooklyn
> Region 11 Council For The Retarded

FOURTH LETTER FROM THE REBBE TO DR. ROBERT WILKES AND PARTICIPANTS IN THE CONFERENCE

ON THE USE OF THE TERM "RETARDED"

Cover Letter

> By the Grace of G-d
> 9th of *Kislev*, 5741
> [November 17, 1980]
> Brooklyn, N. Y.

Dr. R. Wilkes, DSW
Chairman, Brooklyn
Region 11 Council for The Retarded
c/o Coney Island Hospital
2601 Ocean Parkway
Brooklyn, N. Y. 11235

Greeting and Blessing:

This is to acknowledge receipt of your letter of Nov. 13th, with the enclosures in connection with the forthcoming Conference.

Since the matter is of the greatest importance, I have taken time out, despite the pressure of duties, to respond with the enclosed message. You can also supplement it with my past correspondence with you on this subject.

May G-d grant that every one of us should do the utmost along the lines suggested in my message, especially since we have the promise of Divine aid in all such good efforts.

With esteem and blessing

[sig.]

By the Grace of G-d
9 *Kislev*, 5741
Brooklyn, N.Y.

To All Participants in the
Major Conference for the Jewish Community
On Issues and Needs of Jewish Retarded
New York City.

Greeting and Blessing:

I was pleased to be informed of the forthcoming Conference. I trust it will mark a turning point in the attitude of community leaders to Jewish education in general, and to so-called Special Education in particular.

In any discussion relating to the wellbeing of the Jewish community, the primary, indeed pivotal, issue should surely be Jewish Identity—that which truly unites our Jewish people and gives us the strength to survive and thrive in a most unnatural, alien, and all too often hostile environment.

Historically—from the birth of our nation to this day—Jewish identity, in the fullest sense of this term, has been synonymous with traditional Torah-Judaism as our way of life in everyday living. Other factors commonly associated with a national identity, such as language, territory, dress, etc., could not have played a decisive role in Jewish survival, since these changed from time to time and from place to place. The only factor that has not changed throughout our long history has been the Torah and *Mitzvos* which are "our life and the length of our days." The same *Tefillin*, Tzitzis, *Shabbos* and Yom-Tov have been observed by Jews everywhere in all generations. Clearly there is no substitute for the Torah-way as the source and essence of our Jewish people.

Recognizing this prima facie fact, means recognizing that Jewish survival depends on the kind of education that develops and nourishes Jewish identity in the fullest measure. And this must surely be the highest priority of all communal services.

With regard to Jewish retarded—parenthetically, I prefer some such term as "special" people, not simply as a euphemism, but because it would more accurately reflect their situation, especially in view of the fact that in many cases the retardation is limited to the capacity to absorb and assimilate knowledge, while in other areas they may be quite normal or even above average—the Jewish identity factor is even more important, not only per se but also for its therapeutic value. The actual practice of *Mitzvos* in the everyday life provides a tangible way by which these special people of all ages can, despite their handicap, identify with their families and with other fellow Jews in their surroundings, and generally keep in touch with reality. Even if mentally they may not fully grasp the meaning of these rituals, subconsciously they are bound to feel at home in such an environment, and in many cases could participate in such activities also on the conscious level.

To cite one striking example from actual experience during the Festival of Succos this year. As is well known, Lubavitch activists on this occasion reach out to many Jews with Lulov and Esrog, bringing to them the spirit of the Season of Our Rejoicing. This year being a year of Hakhel, I urged my followers to extend this activity as much as possible, to include also Nursing Homes and Senior Citizens' Hotels, as well as other institutions. I was asked, what should be the attitude and approach to persons who are senile or confused, etc. I replied—all the more reason to reach out to them in this tangible way. Well, the reports were profoundly gratifying. Doctors and nurses were astonished to see such a transformation: Persons who had spent countless days in silent immobility, deeply depressed and oblivious to everything around them, the moment they saw a young man walk in with a Lulav and Esrog in his hand suddenly displayed a lively interest, eagerly, grasped the proffered Mitzvah-objects, some of them reciting the blessings from memory, without prompting. The joy in their hearts shone through their faces, which had not known a smile all too long.

One need not look for a mystical explanation of this reaction. Understandably, the sight of something so tangible and clearly associated with the joy of Succos evidently touched and unlocked vivid recollections of experiences that had permeated them in earlier years.

If there is much that can be done along these lines for adult and senior Jews in special situations, how much more so in regard to special children, when every additional benefit, however seemingly small, in their formative years will be compounded many times over as they grow older. In their case it is even more important to bear in mind that while they may be handicapped in their mental and intellectual capacity, and indeed because of it, every possible emphasis should be placed on the tangible and audio-visual aspects of Jewish education in terms of the actual practice of *Mitzvos* and religious observances—as I have discussed this and related aspects at greater length in my correspondence with Dr. R. Wilkes of the Coney Island Hospital.

There is surely no need to elaborate on all above to the participants in the Conference, whose Rabbinic, academic, and professional qualifications in the field of Jewish Education and social services makes them highly sensitive to the problems at hand. I hope and pray that the basic points herein made will serve as guidelines to focus attention on the cardinal issues, and that this Conference will, as mentioned earlier, mark a turning point in attitude, and even more importantly in action vis-a-vis Jewish Education, long overdue.

With prayerful wishes for Hatzlocho, and with esteem and blessing,

[sig.]

FIFTH LETTER FROM DR. WILKES TO THE REBBE

Rabbi Menachem M. Schneerson
770 Eastern Parkway
Brooklyn, N.Y. 11213

Dear Rabbi Schneerson:

The conference (attended by about 250 persons) on "Serving The Jewish Retarded Issues and Needs," sponsored by Federation of Jewish Philanthropies, is over but our work has really just begun. We will again meet on January 15, 1981 to review what has been accomplished and what we must do in the days ahead. At the conclusion of our conference, we made a number of recommendations - a few of them are:

1. Federation has to sponsor more group homes (with Kosher Kitchens) for the retarded;

2. Federation has to allocate more funds to all aspects of Jewish education including special education;

3. We have to influence Hebrew Day Schools not to utilize I.Q. tests to disqualify children and thereby deprive them of a Jewish education;

4. We have to support the UJA - Federation campaign since we cannot expect 'to take' without also 'giving'.

5. We must continue to request the various Boards of Rabbis throughout the city to issue proclamations on behalf of our Jewish retarded and developmentally handicapped.

It was a remarkable conference! I have not had the opportunity to attend many Federation conferences but I can say with pride that for two days (Dec. 10th and 11th) all the participants - Jews from all walks of life - spoke about the very same things you had noted in your message: Torah, Mitzvahs and Yiddeshkeit.

Let me be candid. A few weeks prior to the conference (I had informed Rabbi Groner) I was greatly discouraged by the fact that some orthodox groups, rather abruptly, withdrew their support due to sharp differences in religious perspectives (or principles). I had no idea that our community was so polarized: that various parties have such little respect for each other's viewpoints. Why is it so difficult for our religious groups to accept their own philosophy and practice while at the same time accept (and respect) the contribution that another group can make to Judaism? (I secretly thought that this conference - at which time we all would sit down together as a unified community - would increase the sense of unity within our community and thereby speed the arrival of the Meshiach.) Nevertheless, I left the conference with a feeling of hope and verve.

There was one question, however, raised by a mother that made us pause and reflect as to the nature of our existence: If the primary purpose of existence is to fulfill G-d's commandments; and if a Jew is unable, from childhood, to carry out any of these commandments because of severe physical and mental limitations; what then is the purpose (or meaning) of his/her existence? I would be most appreciative if you would respond to this question.

All our children are entitled to be educated Jewishly. With G-d's help all our goals and dreams for our children will become a reality in our generation.

Once again, thank you for your concern and understanding.

Sincerely Yours,
Robert Wilkes, DSW Member of Federation's
Planning Committee For The Retarded

P.S. Copies of your first letter written to me on 22 Av, 5739 as well as your message and greetings to the conference participants were included in a kit distributed to each participant. Enclosed is a conference kit. Your message was read by myself immediately after our dinner on Wednesday, December 10th. We also learned that you had just a few days previously endorsed the UJA-Federation campaign. Both your en-

dorsement and message generated a sense of excitement and challenge that enhanced our deliberations. cc: Rabbi Dr. Benjamin Sharfman, Chairman Rabbi Isaac Trainin, Director Religious Affairs Committee

FIFTH LETTER FROM
THE REBBE TO DR. ROBERT WILKES

NO ONE CANNOT ACHIEVE

By the Grace of G-d
25th of *Teves*, 5741
Brooklyn, N.Y.

Dr. Robert Wilkes,
Brooklyn, N.Y.

Greeting and Blessing:

Thank you very much for your letter and for the Conference kit received separately. I appreciate the trouble you have taken to report to me on the Conference and its recommendations. May G-d grant that the Conference will produce the desired fruits, even in excess of expectations. Especially as the Zechus Horabim helps, particularly when the Rabim are, in this case, our Jewish youngsters.

With reference to the question at the conclusion of your letter, raised by a mother, to the effect that if the primary purpose of existence is to fulfill G-d's commandments; and if a Jew is unable from childhood to carry out any of these commandments because of physical or mental limitations; what then is the purpose or meaning of his/her existence?

The answer to this question must be sought in the context of a more embracing general problem, of which the above is but one of many possible facets.

It should be remembered that according to the Torah itself, it is impossible for every Jew, as an individual, to fulfill all the

613 *Mitzvos*. Apart from *mitzvos* which are applicable only in Eretz Yisroel and during the time that the Beis Hamikdash is in existence, there are *mitzvos* which are obligatory only to Kohanim for example, while there are *mitzvos* which a Kohen is precluded from fulfilling. But by virtue of the fact that all Jewish people are one entity, like one organism, every individual who fulfills his or her obligations to the extent of their G-d-given capacities, share in the totality of the effort and accomplishment.

A similar principle prevails also in every human society in general, where everyone has to contribute to the common wealth, though each one is necessarily limited in one's capacities, be one a plain farmer, producing food or a scientist or inventor of farm machinery and the like. One who excels in one's particular field of endeavor may be limited or useless in another area. Who is to say which one is more important, which one makes a greater contribution? Only harmonious collaboration and utilization of all human resources make for the utmost completeness and perfection of the society. As for the individual, all that need be said–as indeed our Rabbis have emphasized, is that G-d does not demand of an individual anything that is beyond the individual's natural capacities. It is not for a human being to question why G-d has endowed one individual with greater capacities than another individual.

To return to the subject of the correspondence, namely, the needs of the special children (or the so-called retarded or developmentally limited, as often spoken of), they are, to be sure, limited in certain areas (and who is not?), but there is no reason nor justification, to generalize all into one and the same category of "limited" or "retarded." Human experience is replete with examples of individuals who have been severely limited in some aspects, yet they subsequently excelled and made great extraordinary contributions to society in other aspects.

I am quite convinced that if a proper system of aptitude tests were instituted, to determine the particular skills of our special children at an early age and appropriate classes were established to enable them to develop these skills, the results would be enormously gratifying, if not astounding. Needless to say, such an educational method would greatly enhance their self confidence and general development, not to mention also the fact that it would enable them to make an important contribution to society.

With esteem and blessing,

INVITATION TO ATTEND MELAVA MALKA

Rabbi Groner
Lubavitch
770 Eastern Parkway
Brooklyn, N.Y. 11213

Dear Rabbi Groner,
    On behalf of the parents OTSAR ("Jewish Advocacy for the Retarded") and myself we would like to extend a personal invitation to the Lubavitcher Rebbe, Shlita to attend our first Milava Malke, 12 Adar, 5742. Our guest speaker will be Rabbi Dr. Immanuel Jakobovitz, Chief Rabbi of the United Kingdom.
    Our friend and colleague, Dr. Robert Wilkes, has informed us that only recently one of his parents, Mrs. P. Gaffney together with Dr. G. Schwartz and Dr. Wilkes spoke at a Beth Rivka Parents association meeting in Crown Heights on December 8, 1981; and that the Lubavitch school principals from Brooklyn have been working closely with Rabbi Martin Schloss regarding workshops on 'learning disabilities' and 'resource rooms' for either Jewish or English studies or both.

It was on 22 Av, 5739 that Rabbi Menachem Schneerson, Shlita sent Dr. Wilkes a comprehensive and some prophetic statement that encourage all of us to increase our special sons and daughters in all aspects of Yiddishkeit. That letter was the beginning — the catalyst — which induced other Rabbis and communal leaders to take a public stand; and it was again the Lubavitcher Rebbe, Shlita, who sent us words of support and blessing when together with the Federation of Jewish philanthropies we conducted a historic major citywide conference on the needs of our Jewish developmentally handicapped. Once again we come to the Lubavitcher Rebbe, Shlita, and the Lubavitch community to ask for your prayers, your concern, and your active participation.

Please feel free to contact Dr. Wilkes, who will, I'm certain, be ready and prepared to do whatever he can to facilitate your efforts. We hope and pray that our work on behalf of our special children will merit the coming of Moshiach.

Respectfully yours,

Here ends the correspondence of the Rebbe and Dr. Wilkes.

ASSISTING THE SENILE AND MENTALLY CONFUSED BY EVOKING FOND MEMORIES THROUGH TANGIBLE OBJECTS

...I offer you the following salient example of an actual experience that occurred during this year's festival of *Sukkos*:

As known, Lubavitcher chassidim utilize this occasion to reach many Jews in order to provide them with both the opportunity to perform the commandment of "*lulav* and *esrog*" as well as help them experience the joy of this festival, the "Festival of Our Rejoicing."

Since this is a year of *Hakhel*, I asked my chassidim to expand these activities to the greatest extent possible and to include in their activities visits to nursing and retirement homes, as well as other institutions. I was asked about what position should be taken regarding the senile and the mentally confused, etc., and I responded that surely these individuals should be approached — even more so than others — as this is an opportunity to reach them through something tangible and concrete.

The results were most gratifying. Doctors and nurses were astounded to observe such a turnabout — people who had spent countless days immobile and mute, utterly despondent and depressed and unaware of their surroundings, suddenly became alert and showed interest upon beholding a young person entering with a *lulav* and *esrog* in hand.

They eagerly grasped these objects, many of them reciting the blessings from memory, without having to be told at all the text of the blessings. Their joy was clearly visible on their faces, faces that had not seen a smile on them for such a long time.

There is no need to find a mystical explanation for their response. As is readily understandable, the sight of something so tangible and that was so obviously connected to the joy of *Sukkos* evidently evoked and revealed fond memories and experiences of years past....

(From a letter of the Rebbe, dated 9 Kislev, 5741)

chapter 9

HEALING THROUGH MEDITATION
AND RELAXATION TECHNIQUES

KOSHER MEDITATION

There is an issue connected with the physical and psychological health of many Jews, that demands attention. It is quite possible that these words will have no effect. Nevertheless, the health of a Jew is such an important matter, that efforts should be made even when there is not a sure chance of success.

This issue is the idea of meditation. Meditation has its roots in the very beginning of the Jewish heritage. The Torah commentaries explain that Avraham and the other Patriarchs chose to be shepherds so that they could spend their time in solitude.

Their lives were not simple, physical lives. On the contrary, they were totally given over to the service of G-d to the point where they were called "G-d's chariot." [That metaphor was chosen because a chariot has no will of its own and is totally controlled by its driver; similarly their lives were totally controlled by G-d.]

They chose a profession that would allow them to live such a spiritual existence. Therefore, they became shepherds, spending their days in the fields, in solitude, rather than becoming involved in the hubbub of life in the cities.

The same holds true today. There are certain aspects of psychological health and tranquility that can be attained by taking oneself out of contact with the surrounding hullabaloo and tumult of life.

By retreating into solitude (not necessarily leaving the city) and by withdrawing into seclusion for a period of time, one may attain psychological health and peace of mind. This manner of behavior strengthens the individual and guards his mental health.

This process involves withdrawing from the clamor and tumult of the street and meditating on an object that brings about serenity and peace of mind.

The Torah's statement,[1] "Behold I have set before you life and goodness, death and evil" is applicable to all matters. Every aspect of life can be utilized for the good or for the opposite.

For example, the sun, moon and stars are necessary for life to exist on earth, bringing about a multitude of good. However, these celestial bodies have also been worshipped as deities.

One may ask (as the *Talmud* does):[2] "Since these celestial bodies have been worshipped as false deities, shouldn't they be destroyed?" The *Talmud's* answer is most instructive: "Should the world be destroyed because of these fools?!"

The same applies to meditation. Though essentially positive, meditation can also be used in a destructive manner. There are those who have connected meditation to actually bowing down to an idol, or to a man, and worshipping it or him, offering incense before them, and so on.

These cults have spread throughout the United States and throughout *Eretz Yisrael* as well. Some of these cults have been called by a refined name, "transcendental meditation,"

---

1   *Devarim* 30:15.

2   *Avodah Zarah* 54b.

thereby implying that it is something above limits, above our limited intellect.

However, they have also incorporated into their practices the offering of incense and other actions that clearly come under the heading of idolatry.

Since we are living in the darkness of Exile, many Jewish youth have fallen into this snare. Before they became involved with this cult, they were troubled and disturbed; the cult was able to relate to them and offer them peace of mind.

However, their form of meditation is connected with idolatry: burning incense, bowing to a guru, etc. Since these idolatry aspects are not publicized, there are those who have not raised their voices in protest.

Moreover, they are unsure if such a protest would be met with success, and since no one has asked for their opinion, they think to themselves, "Why protest and enmesh oneself in a questionable situation?"

However, while those who should be protesting remain silent, Jewish youth are becoming involved in idolatry, a sin so severe that the Torah declares that one should sacrifice his life rather than worship idols. Moreover, this scourge is spreading, ensnaring youth and adults alike.

Additionally, since "One sin leads to another," even those who are not yet involved in the more severe and more clearly idolatrous forms of this group will eventually be drawn into this aspect of idolatry in their search of a "holier" and more "sacred" guru-deity.

A program must therefore be organized to spread "kosher meditation." While there are those who argue against this, maintaining that "kosher meditation" might well lead to "non-kosher meditation," the fact of the matter is that this is not so.

It is opposite the spirit of Judaism and especially opposite the spirit of *Chassidus* to withhold assistance from anyone in need of it; should someone be in need, we are obligated to help him. And when the individual does not even realize that he requires help, the necessity to assist him becomes even greater.

However, the above debate ignores the main issue: We are not dealing here with providing a means of approved meditation necessarily for those who wish to begin meditating. Rather, there are Jews who have already fallen for this deception, and the simplest way to draw them out of it is by providing them with a kosher alternative.

Clearly, the Torah obligates us to do so — and this is aside from the fact that by doing so we are fulfilling the commandment of healing a fellow Jew and "Loving your neighbor as yourself.".…

In instituting this program, two major factors must be taken into consideration:

Meditation should only be used by those who are in need of it; a psychologically healthy individual does not need to practice this. To the contrary, a healthy and calm individual who begins to withdraw within himself through meditation will only harm his mental health.

A parallel to this notion can be found in the *Talmud*. The *Talmud* tells about the laborers of Mechuzah who were accustomed to hard work and carrying heavy loads. When they were unable to do so, it caused them to become ill.

Here as well, those who have no need of taking time away from their productive labor and rewarding lifestyle in order to withdraw and relax through meditation will invariably find it to be disadvantageous.

The manner of meditation required by all is that which is part and parcel of one's spiritual service. Thus we find the directive in the *Shulchan Aruch* that prior to prayer an individual should meditate on "G-d's greatness and man's insignificance." This meditation, however, is one that has fixed times — prior to prayer — and specific goals, and not the calming of one's nerves.

The second crucial feature is that the meditation must be based on a kosher idea or a Torah concept, e.g., "*Shema Yisrael*," and the concepts implied therein. This will lead the individual to a greater awareness of G-d's greatness and man's inconsequentiality — a meditation that is in keeping with the general meditation preceding prayer.

Furthermore, since all forms of healing possess a certain degree of control exerted by the healer over the person being healed, care must be taken to assure that the professional guiding the meditation has a clear and precise knowledge of what is permitted according to Jewish law and what things are prohibited, as the latter may lead to idolatrous practice.

Additionally, the professional must be conscious of the fact that meditation has much in common with other medical therapies:

Drugs and medications are only valuable if one limits their quantity; their excessive use can only bring harm and not benefit. Moreover, medication is only indicated when the individual is unwell; once he is healed, it is harmful to continue taking the medication. Meditation must be similarly regulated....

In view of the current situation, psychologists, psychoanalysts and the like have a sacred duty to advance their knowledge of meditation and begin working on developing a kosher program of meditation. Moreover, as we live in a country where publicity plays such a large role, efforts must be made to publicize this manner of treatment in the broadest possible way.

In addition, this form of treatment should not be connected in any way with other side issues, important as they may be.

For example, there are those who maintain that meditation must be connected with the esoteric and hidden portion of Torah. Meditation on the secrets of Torah is indeed very important, particularly now when the wellsprings of *Chassidus* must continually be made known to all.

However, this is not the issue at hand. There are Jews who are involved in idolatry who must be saved. This is the top priority. If one begins by teaching them the secrets of the Torah, it is most likely that the majority of them will not respond. Even those who might show an interest should first be sundered from idolatry.

While the above is the responsibility of all, however, [this is not a task that can be entrusted to everyone, for] should a novice begin studying about meditation, it would take a long time for him to master the subject. Therefore, psychologists, psychoanalysts and the like should be turned to, trying to interest them in teaching and spreading "kosher meditation."

They should be told that thousands of Jews are being drawn into the worship of idols, offering incense, believing in gurus as deities, etc. They thus have a sacred task (and surely they desire to do this on their own as well) to heal these people.

All that is necessary for them to do is to expand their

knowledge into a field already related to their own, that of meditation. After a short amount of time, they will master the techniques of this treatment, since they already have much practical experience in helping such individuals.

If publicized adequately, this campaign will be met with immediate success, saving so many who stand at a crossroads and who do not mean to live in opposition to Judaism. When these individuals will be offered the opportunity to choose between a permitted and forbidden manner of treatment, they will invariably choose the former.

This success will, in turn, also attract those who have already become enmeshed in the forbidden form of meditation to also begin practicing "kosher meditation."...

(Excerpted from Sichos Kodesh 5739, Vol. III, p. 314ff.)

THE PERMITTED AND PROHIBITED ASPECTS OF "MEDITATION"

It has been some time now since I have been informed of the ruling in *Eretz Yisrael* concerning the absolute prohibition of the various forms of ministrations done by a guru, including seclusion, meditation, and the like.

The above-mentioned ruling is based on the fact that this form of ministration by gurus includes aspects of idolatry, or at least a semblance (*avizrai'hu*) of idolatry — idolatry being one of the three sins that are so severe that the Torah declares that one should sacrifice his life rather than commit them.

However, the aspect of seclusion and meditation, etc., in and of themselves is not something novel that they discovered, G-d forbid, nor does the successful implementation of these measures depend on them, Heaven forfend. As to their offering incense and the like — this is not important to the achievement of meditation, as one can readily understand.

Therefore, in accordance with the saying of our Sages, of blessed memory, "Should the world be destroyed because of these fools?!" my suggestion is the following:

It would be worthwhile and proper — and possibly even necessary — for you (either doing so yourself or having it done by those who follow your instructions) to contact G-d-fearing doctors and other experts in the field of "nerves," peace of mind, and mental illness, and place upon them the obligation (more properly — the merit and opportunity) that they enhance their knowledge of healing and treatment through seclusion, introspection and the like.

Having done so, they should then publicize this to the greatest extent possible, particularly since in addition to their ability to then heal so many individuals who are ill and in need of this form of therapy, this will also serve as a good medium to sever them from the "gurus" who draw them close through using this form of healing, as they will see that the same benefits can be received without incense and through a G-d-fearing man or woman....

(Likkutei Sichos, Vol. XXXVI, p. 335)

A SCOURGE THAT IS SPREADING

...It surprises me that I have yet to receive any news regarding any actions taken concerning the "healings" of yoga, the gurus, and all that is related thereto, [particularly,] after you notified me some time ago that you spoke about this matter or conveyed it to Professor ... Surely you are aware that this scourge is spreading: the event in Tzfas, the letter of the Sephardic Chief Rabbi, *and more.*

(Likkutei Sichos, Vol. XXXVI, p. 336)

AN IMMINENT DANGER AND ITS PROPER RESPONSE

...The main problem is the immediate danger (facing the many Jews who are receiving therapy involved with aspects of idolatry). Thus it is understandable that the first steps to be taken are that of saving them from this danger — this requires immediate and ongoing action.

One of the methods and ways of doing so [immediately] is that all those who already have permission to perform a similar form of therapy devote particular attention as to how they can perform the above [meditation] therapy in a kosher manner.

Moreover, it is important that these doctors and others as well publicize that this particular doctor is offering this particular form of therapy. They should also seek to influence all other doctors who practice mental healing that they too interest themselves in providing such [kosher] therapy to those patients who are in need of it.

[Once this is done, it is] also [important] to establish a connection between these doctors so that they be able to be of assistance to one another in therapeutic techniques, that they be able to offer encouragement to one another, and similar matters.

An in-depth study of this form of therapy, establishment of a general institute [of kosher meditation] and the like are all fine and necessary.

However, all this requires preparation (assembling material from those who have already been practicing this and from those who will be doing so in the future; acquiring a thorough knowledge of the literature that has already been written about meditation; consulting the experts throughout the world and doing so with proper honor to each of them).

This, of course, cannot be done in haste (in order not to anger the experts, etc.) and must therefore be done step by step. This is not so with regard to the methods I proposed above that can be implemented immediately — and the sooner, the better....

(Likkutei Sichos, Vol. XXXVI, p. 336)

ATTRACT AS MANY INDIVIDUALS AS POSSIBLE

Thank you for your letter of 13 *Adar* II. I appreciate your comprehensive response to my letter and memorandum on the need to organize widespread use of T.M. and similar techniques in psychotherapy compatible with the Torah with the double objective of making such therapy available to Jewish patients in a kosher way and at the same time saving numerous Jews from getting involved with *Avodah Zora* as now commonly practised in the USA.

Needless to say, I noted your suggestions and observations in this connection with understandable interest.

In reply, let me first say that, as a general principle, so long as the said two objectives can best be served, whatever project is determined to be most effective is most desirable, and, of course, acceptable to me.

There are, however, some points in your response which need careful assessment. For instance, the suggestion that an Institute employing the said healing techniques might be linked with a strictly orthodox, even Lubavitch, orientation should be examined in light of it being a possible, or even likely, deterrent for many candidates who might hesitate to turn to such an Institute for fear that it may impose upon them religious demands and commitments which they are not yet prepared to accept.

The above is not to say that the idea should be rejected out of hand, since there may be many individuals who would not be deterred by it. But I believe that if the project is to attract a wider circle of candidates for therapy, it would have a wider acceptance if it is not overtly tied in with such an orientation, or discipline; at any rate, not in the initial stage.

Needless to say, the emphasis is on the overt orientation of the projected Institute, which should have no religious or other preconditions for anyone seeking its services. But the Institute itself should, of course be run in strict keeping with the Torah, with a kosher, indeed glat-kosher, kitchen, strict *Shabbos* observance, with *Mezuzos* on all doors - just as there are glat-kosher Hotels and institutions.

With regard to the basic point you make in your letter, namely, that most people for whom our plan is envisaged consider themselves "normal" and would not be interested in a program that offers professional (medical) services, but would prefer a more simplistic setup for relaxation, etc., — this should certainly be taken into account, since the ultimate goals of our plan would not be affected. And, if as you suggest, this would be the more practical setup for attracting more people and achieving our two objectives — healing and elimination of *Avodah Zora* — then, by all means, this method should be given due consideration....

Your further comments will be welcome, and many thanks again.

(From a letter of the Rebbe, dated 21 Adar II, 5738)

SEND ME A BUDGET

...Now to the main subject of our correspondence, namely saving Jews from getting involved in *Avodah Zora* through T.M. and the like by offering them a kosher alternative.

With reference to your letter of April 9, I would like to make the following observations:

Although a well-planned and systematic approach is generally required to ensure the success of any project, I do not think that we can afford to delay too long the implementation of our plan through time-consuming preparations, and for two reasons: Firstly, every day that the plan is not in operation means so many more Jews turning to those unholy cults, and there is no other sure way of preventing or discouraging this. Secondly, and this is also a weighty consideration, every new project is provisional by nature, for it is expected that as it progresses there would be need for changes and improvements, which is common experience in various fields, medicine, science, business, etc.

2. I note in your letter that your discussions with your colleagues have advanced to the point of forming an ad hoc committee. I therefore believe that the stage can now be set to start immediately a pilot clinic or similar facility, to start offering actual treatment, on the basis of your and your colleagues' professional expertise and mutual consultations. The pilot project should be set up in a way that allows for ample flexibility for modification and change as may be necessary.

As indicated, I will be able to provide funding for the initial stage, within limitations. You will no doubt send me a tentative budget of the initial outlay, with an estimate of the period of time it may take until the setup becomes self-supporting. Indeed, I am confident that before long it will not only be self-supporting, but also profitable, considering the popularity of techniques involved. But it is important to start in a way that will not inhibit the effectiveness and development of the project, even if it costs much more.

3. With regard to specifics, I do not think it advisable to use the term "mystic" for the planned healing center, since the goal is to attract the greatest number of Jews and save them from *Avodah Zora*, and the said term might discourage some. Moreover, generally mysticism connotes something that lies beyond the pale of human comprehension, while the therapeutic benefits of the techniques are quite understandable rationally. Besides, to emphasize the mystical aspect would leave the door open also, *lehavdil*, to non-Jewish mystical cults.

For the same reason it is advisable to be circumspect in regard to the description of the techniques to be used in the healing center. For example, you mention the use of "*Mikvos.*" while it is not in my domain to assess the therapeutic effect of relaxation in a hot *Mikvah*, I fear that to include a <u>mikvah</u> "officially" in the regimen might be suspected — by some people, at least - that it is a gimmick to involve them in *Mitzvos.* I think that veiling it in some such term as "immersion", hot <u>bath,</u> and the like would entirely allay such suspicion.

As for calling the healing center by the name "Noam" — it is a name already in use by various organizations and journals. Another suitable name would have to be found, but there is no need to make a final decision on this right away.

Finally, let me relieve you of any apprehension that you might be "pushing" me on this matter. On the contrary, in connection with such a vital project "pushing" could only be all to the good, since time is of the essence, as I emphasized above....

(From a letter of the Rebbe, dated 11 Sivan, 5738)

addendum 1

EDUCATION — A MORAL OBLIGATION

EDUCATION — A MORAL OBLIGATION

Man,[1] the creature created in G-d's image, differs from other creations, above all in his soul. Man, like all other species, has a body which by its very finite corporeal essence drags him down to the level of animal; his bodily functions paralleling those of an animal. It is through the soul, and the mind which is a reflection of the soul, that man soars above the corporeal and reaches the loftiest heights. This is the destiny of man, the battle that has been fought since man first set foot on this earth, using his intellect to master the animal and to show that he is indeed . . . man.

This struggle is not an easy one, for the corporeality of the body and the world is very tangible, and encountered at every turn. The matters of the soul, on the other hand, are more obscure; and a greater effort is demanded in order to discern the presence of the Maker in all things. The supreme instrument of man's ability to rise higher than the physical, the intellect, is the key to winning this struggle.

Undoubtedly, recent times have shown tremendous progress in man's mastery of nature. We have witnessed an explosion of knowledge that has dwarfed the achievements of previous generations, bringing with it marvels of modern technology.

Unfortunately however, knowledge is not synonymous

---

1   This essay was originally printed in Sichos In English 5741 (12 *Tammuz*).

with understanding; and moral development has not kept pace with technical progress. The knowledge that could have been put to so many constructive uses has instead been channeled into, at best, wasteful, useless activities, and at worst, destructive acts of violence. A possible blessing has been perverted into a curse. Those bent on acts of destruction, whether from sheer greed, malice, or insanity, can now, thanks to modern day technology, easily wreak their havoc not only on their immediate surroundings, but exert influence on the entire community of mankind.

The failure to control this growing lawlessness is not limited to a few individuals. In the last few decades, and especially in the past few years, international tension and frictions have accelerated at frightening proportions. The soaring crime rate among individuals has evolved into a trend of national and international banditry, with wars raging across the face of the world. Hardly a nation has been left untouched by the horrors of violence, both on an individual and national scale, and the world seems helpless to resist. A blanket of doom seems to have settled on the earth, and under its cover, outrageous acts are carried out with impunity. And with violence breeding more violence, the perpetrators of this terror have only one regret — that they neither did nor could inflict more damage. Their appetite for money, territory, or just plain mayhem grows insatiable, and the prospects for control grow dimmer. Police forces are increased and armies strengthened, all in a desperate attempt to retain control of a rapidly declining situation.

And the cause for the spreading increase in crime? Innumerable commissions have been set up, countless study groups have examined this problem. And the result? Total obfuscation! As many "answers" have been offered as studies made, all sharing one common point. Each strove to find some hidden cause, some deep unnatural reason — while ignoring the most obvious and true of them all. In a single word: education. It is only through proper moral and ethical education that we can be assured of children growing up to be good, productive citizens. We turn our attention, then, to an analysis of the difference between past and present education. A change for the good in the education of a child will result in a better adult; and so with the reverse.

Only a few scant generations ago, most parents were G-d-fearing folk, believing with absolute faith in a G-d Who is the Master of the world. Not a strange belief, for it was upon this very principle that the U.S.A. was founded. The founding fathers possessed an absolute trust in G-d, a G-d Who was real and omnipresent, not a G-d Who politely resided in books and philosophical conjectures. So strong was their belief that trust in G-d brings success, that they uprooted themselves from their homelands, forsook all ties with the past, and journeyed to find a place in which they could serve G-d with full religious freedom.

Such a faith did not need to be taught in school. It was inculcated in children from the moment of birth; they lived it as naturally as they breathed. The very conduct of their parents and grandparents conveyed the same message — the world has not been left untended, there is a Master Who rules. Any mention of religion in school was unnecessary and inconsequential next to this complete and total education.

As time passed, the emphasis on such trust weakened. But full belief was still there: to bless and praise G-d for the food eaten or to say one's prayers at night — these things were still taken for granted. It was only later that religious instruction in schools became necessary. And still, teachers were mainly G-d-fearing people, who, by their very demeanor and behavior, inculcated their students with a belief and trust in G-d.

It has only been in very recent years that religious instruction in schools has been forbidden. No mention of G-d, not even a simple nondenominational prayer is permitted. And the results of this attitude are painfully evident. Lack of awareness of a higher Deity, and the resultant void of moral and ethical training, has led to a generation of selfish, egoistical children, whose sole aim in life is the pursuit of pleasure. And if that pursuit conflicts with responsibilities, such responsibilities are discarded. The inevitable result is a generation which disregards others, with a resultant callousness towards all the higher things in life. The indulgence of one's desires is the only object of importance, and all other considerations are swept aside. No wonder that theft, violence, even murder, have become so commonplace, accompanied by a complete breakdown in what was once an orderly, constructive way of life. It is but the bitter reaping of a harvest so blithely and carelessly sown.

The beginning of all this starts in the home, with the parents who so unwisely indulge every whim and fancy of their child. Led to believe that despite whatever he or she will do, each will still be regarded as a "good" boy or "good" girl, such children grow up wild and unrestrained, bereft of any cognizance that the world was not created for their sole benefit. And it is not entirely their fault! It is the parents who, abdicating their responsibility of rearing their young in the proper manner, have given spawn to a generation of unbridled passions. And to make matters worse, it is all cloaked in the pious guise of "Constitutional rights!" Any attempt to remonstrate with parents is met with cries of indignation against intrusion of privacy guaranteed by the Constitution. The child can run loose, growing up to be a potential menace to society — but their right to educate their children in their own way, however harmful that may be, must remain inviolate.

The inevitable result has reached such a degree as to produce a situation that would be laughable if it were not so tragic. A recently released report states that the number of incidents of students attacking teachers has declined in some schools! The truth of this report is immaterial. [Parenthetically, it is probable that rather than a decrease in the actual number, the truth is that teachers are *afraid* to report such incidents.] The point is the utter unreality of the situation. Even ten years ago, it was inconceivable for a student to physically strike a teacher. And yet, statistics are now being released to show that the number of such incidents is. . . decreasing! Can a more damning indictment of our educational system be found?

Let us emphasize again that the cause is clear and defined. It is the craven attitude of parents and educators alike, who refuse to educate their children with the knowledge of a higher Being Who is omnipotent and omnipresent, and to Whom an account must eventually be rendered. They have prostituted themselves before an idol of their own making, sacrificing entire generations of children on the altar of "freedom." But it has quickly become obvious that their idol has feet of clay, and their obeisance to it an obscene rite of stubborn refusal to admit wrongdoing.

A further smoke-screen is thrown up with declarations of "human rights," in which it is forbidden to educate a child in the proper manner because it might infringe on his or her "rights." We do not refer to an education that actively teaches a child to steal or commit an offense — it is much more subtle. The very fact that a child is brought up to believe that he alone is the only person that matters, with a perfect right to all the desires of his heart, leads very quickly to actions that, in pursuit of this goal, can easily harm others.

The pity and shame of it all is that this is a country which has been blessed with a great deal of knowledge. This knowledge could have been used to better the world, but instead, has in many instances been perverted to further an individual's own selfish interests, even at the cost of another. In matters of morals and ethics, there are no more standards, no absolutes by which to judge behavior. A strange thing indeed. In matters of physical health, no one would dream of consulting an ignorant layman, but would always go to a competent physician, with years of study and practice. Yet when it comes to morals and ethics, matters of the soul, everyone is an expert! Anyone may advance an opinion, regardless of whether his life has been lived according to ideals of justice and morality. And people are, incredibly enough, ready and willing to entrust in such hands the education of that most precious of possessions — their children.

Know then, that each and every parent and educator has been given strength by G-d to change all of this. Changes *can* be made in their children's education, and darkness can be turned into light, foolishness into wisdom. In turn, it is the duty, and privilege, of the leaders of this nation, whether on a national, state, or local level, to help parents in their task of properly educating their children. The first priority of this country must be given to ensuring that its children grow up to be healthy, both physically and spiritually. And the best way to carry this out is a nondenominational declaration,[2] at the start of each day, stating that there is an omnipotent, omniscient G-d, who demands proper conduct from us all.

To return to where we started: Man has the ability to reach the loftiest heights, or to sink to the lowest depths. He can be an animal, or a man, created in the Divine image; a wild unrestrained beast who must devour everything he sees, or a man that lives a decent productive life, contributing fully to society. The choice is clear cut. And the only way to ensure that people will choose the right path is to educate them when they are still young, forming their character before it is too late. It is an awesome task to be sure. But the stakes are too high and the alternative too terrible to allow any faintness of heart. If we have but the courage and the will to make an honest effort, then we can be sure that G-d will assist us in our endeavors, and this sacred mission will be crowned with success.

---

2   As seen in the following essay, the Rebbe later redirected the focus to instituting a moment of silence in schools.

addendum 2

SOCIETY'S GREAT HOPE:
"A MOMENT OF SILENCE"

SOCIETY'S GREAT HOPE: "A MOMENT OF SILENCE"

Is[1] there an antidote for the problems that plague society today?

How do we ensure that the children of this generation will grow up to be responsible citizens of the world?

How do we balance the self-centered attitude of the "Me" generation?

Is there a means of assuring that civilization will continue to follow the norms of justice and the socially acceptable rules that have become the pillars of a just social order?

The answer to these and other troubling and heartbreaking questions facing the world today may be found by first recognizing and accepting certain objective truths about ourselves and our universe.

At the heart of the response and at the base of the solution lies the need for the universal acceptance of, and firm faith in, the Creator and Ruler of the world. This bedrock of belief will provide the immutable foundation upon which may be built the assurance of future civilized conduct, in accordance with socially acceptable norms, laws of justice and propriety, and sensible rules of human rights and privileges.

---

1   This essay was originally printed in Sichos In English 5746 (*Simchas Torah*).

THE NATURE OF MAN

Scripture describes for us the primitive nature of the uneducated and untrained human being:

> The inclination of man's heart is evil from his youth. *(Bereishis 8:21)*

To this Rashi adds:

> From the moment the fetus bestirs itself to have an independent existence the evil inclination is given to it. *(loc. cit.)*

This being the case, will the average child have any impulse or motivation to refrain from fulfilling his desires or lusts — even when it means taking something which belongs to a friend or to a teacher? This problem is especially prevalent among American children who have been given the notion that they are the "chosen creations" — certainly *everything is theirs* for the grabbing.

While the child may be aware of the existence of the police or some other restrictive force — he is not stymied, because he considers himself smart enough to outwit the policeman.

THE ONLY SOLUTION

The only solution to guarantee that this child will follow the laws of justice and morality is to inculcate in him the recognition of, and belief in, the Creator and Ruler of the world.

The child must be given to understand that the world is not a jungle, for there is a Creator and Master who sees and evaluates all his actions, there is the "Eye that sees and the ear that hears." For *this* reason he must conduct himself in a civilized and just manner.

WHAT ABOUT SECULAR EDUCATION?

We should add, that in our generation it is redundant to cite proofs, to *refute* the claim that we can rely on the study of the physical science or social sciences in order to refine or moderate a child's conduct.

This generation has witnessed the awesome destruction wrought by the nation which boasted the greatest advancement in science and philosophy — they *studied morality* and *produced the greatest murderers,* whose bestiality was unmatched in the annals of human history. Why, they even used their advanced scientific and technological expertise to expedite their murderous designs with alacrity, efficiency and bestial inhumanity.

Scientific knowledge and worldly wisdom are *tools,* which may be utilized for *good* or *bad* — all depending on the character of the person using them. A person of fine character and good attributes — will use his scientific and secular knowledge to improve the state of the world. While in the opposite dimension, the one who follows the will and wile of his evil impulse is capable of utilizing science and knowledge in a negative manner, to increase evil and suffering, in an immeasurable way. *We are witnesses to this fact!* (Affliction shall not rise up a second time. Nachum 1:9)

These phenomena have clearly proved that civilized behavior cannot be based solely on human intellect or social teachings — only on faith in the Creator and Master of the world.

THE ROLE OF THE SCHOOL

It therefore follows, that this faith must be imbued in our children while they are in school — for is it not the role and goal of the school to educate and mold the child to be worthy of the name *human being?!*

In past generations the role of the school was only geared to imparting knowledge, because moral values were imbued at home, by parents. In our generation, however, and especially in recent times, parents are bogged down with the problems of making a living and communal activities, and consequently, they do not nurture or train their children in moral values, but rely on the schools to fill the vacuum. It therefore becomes the responsibility of the schools and the professional educators to assume that role and to impart the moral education in addition to the three R's.

We see this fact so crystally clear in this country, where over the past so years the spiritual and moral standards of our youth have deteriorated astonishingly, from one extreme to the other. In outlook and in action, we see a tremendous increase in anti-social (almost sub-human) behavior among the youth.

The *sole reason?* — a lack of belief in the Creator and Ruler of the world. In the earlier generations, when each person believed in G-d, he educated his child likewise, but today we have a generation of parents whose parents left that moral responsibility to the schools, no wonder that their children are in such a sorry state!

THE BACKLASH OF LAXITY

In the end, the parents will suffer the backlash of their laxity, for just as the child steals from others, he will also steal from his own parents, especially since he knows them to be merciful; so he fears no punishment. It is concerning such mercy that Scripture states:

Hands of compassionate women have boiled their own children. *(Eicha 4:10)*

And the wisest of men proclaimed:

He that spares his rod hates his son. *(Mishlei 14:24)*

How can the moral condition of our children be corrected. By placing attention and emphasis on inculcating the faith in the Creator. And this must be done *in every school* which is concerned with the education and training of children and their initiation into the socially acceptable norms of society.

WHAT ABOUT THE PRINCIPLE OF RELIGION AND STATE?

Enter those who 'care' for the "basic principles" of our republic. They argue that to teach belief in the Creator is against the statute and principle of separation of religion and state.

This argument has no basis in fact!

Any principle or rule in a democratic society exists *only* for the *good* of the *people*. When the good of the people demands a change (or modified interpretation) of the rule — then the rule *must* be *adapted* or *changed* to match the need.

A society which lays down the principle of the separation of religion and state really means that it wants to provide a framework for *freedom* of *religion* — without the interference of government. That was the true intention of this hallowed statute; not the opposite — to restrict or prohibit the opportunity for expression of religious practice and belief!

Yet, there are still those who stubbornly want to protect the 'letter' of the law *against* the *good* of the *people* — and in total disregard for the *spirit* of the law — *religious freedom!*

THE ANSWER: A "MOMENT OF SILENCE"

It was in response to this opposition that the suggestion for a "Moment of Silence" was propounded. When a "Moment of Silence" is instituted at the start of the school day there is no compromising of the neutrality of the state, for this is *not prayer*, but *silence!*

Knowing that school time is devoted to education, the child realizes that the moment of silence must be dedicated to the most important things in this life: his outlook on life, and his belief in the Creator and Ruler of the world: as per the instructions which *his parents will* give him.

I want to stress that this must be at the *start* of the *day* to emphasize the magnitude of the subject. At any other time of the day it would not have the proper impact — the child would contemplate on this last lesson.

Since the substance of this reflection time would depend on the free will of each individual, without teacher, supervisor or government intervention, it does not represent an incursion of the state into the free exercise of religion by the individual.

WHAT TO MEDITATE ON?

Even those parents who do not have the time to train their children, will still find the time to suggest some momentous subject to their children to think about, not "lollipops" or "football," or the "prowess" of attacking other children. Rather they will instruct their children to meditate about such matter what will make them worthy of the name *human being* — not wild beasts of the jungle — in a proper, civilized manner.

The children will remember that they heard their parents tell them of the "Eye that sees and the ear that hears."

At some point in this crusade there were well-meaning representatives in government who tried to introduce a "Moment of *Prayer*" — this was doomed to fail, for "If you grab a lot you cannot hold it." *(Rosh Hashanah* 4b) In fact, that bill has recently been rejected. Good that it was — for a "Moment of Prayer" might create a scenario where a teacher or supervisor could impose his particular form of prayer, or his religion's version of prayer on the students — something which would be wholly unacceptable.

Now that the first bill has been defeated the time is propitious to work for a "Moment of Silence."

ACT — AROUSE PUBLIC OPINION

Therefore:

Public opinion is very important — everyone in government is sensitive to a wave of public interest, the people at the top, the Senators, Congressmen etc. It is therefore very important, that this time, the circles of government in Washington should see a swell of public opinion to institute a "Moment of Silence" at the beginning of the school day.

Preferably this momentum should come from the children themselves. They should send individual letters or sign petitions wherein they will express their desire for a "Moment of Silence." And, since they are not the ones who make the decisions, although it pertains to them, and since we are a democratic nation — they should therefore turn to their representatives *to act* on *their behalf* and institute a "Moment of Silence." Certainly this will have a strong impact on all who receive these petitions.

If the effort will be explained in this manner there are good chances for success. There is the added factor in that the President and those who are influenced by him, look favorably on this proposal and they too want a bill that will provide this opportunity. It is only necessary to make the small move of showing them that public opinion is on their side.

ACTION — LETTERS AND PETITIONS

There is much to say, but the deed is of the essence. Letters and petitions must be sent to the Members of the Senate and House of Representatives (after first consulting with those who worked on this before, and know from experience what to do).

And may this involvement bring the hoped-for success in a great measure, so that it will happen naturally and without any problems; and quickly — "An hour earlier is always better."

May it be the Will of G-d that there will be no need to speak of this matter in the future, as it will be rectified very soon, and through this act we will merit speedily the complete and true redemption for the whole world. It will usher in an era of no famine and no war, no jealously and no hate for all the good things will be plentiful and we will devote our time to knowing the L-rd. The Jewish people will have the free time to be involved in the study of Torah and its wisdom. This will come about because of our work on behalf of mankind.

(Sorry to say, there are also Jews who need the Moment of Silence, because so many Jewish children still attend public schools. Their parents are insensitive to the importance of a religious education. We must encourage them and strengthen their faith — but in broader terms this subject is important for Jews and non-Jews.)

And may we merit the blessings of the Holy One blessed be He — "and I will pour out for you blessings immeasurable." *(Malachi 3:10)*

לעילוי נשמת
ההר"ח הרה"ת ר' **יונה**
בן ההר"ח הרה"ת ר' מאיר ע"ה
אבצן
מנהל ועד שיחות באנגלית
למעלה מארבעים שנה
שבהמשך פעולותיו בהפצת המעיינות
נזכה לגאולה השלימה תיכף ומיד ממש

❧

נדפס על ידי
הרוצה בעילום שמו

לזכות כ"ק אדמו"ר נשיא דורנו

❧

נדפס על ידי
הרוצה בעילום שמו